The World of an Island

The World of an
Island

PHILIP COXON

illustrated by Michèle Coxon

Faber and Faber London

First published in 1977
by Faber and Faber Limited
3 Queen Square London WC1
Filmset and printed in Great Britain by
BAS Printers Limited, Over Wallop, Hampshire
All rights reserved

© *Philip Coxon 1977*
Illustrations © *Faber and Faber 1977*

British Library Cataloguing in Publication Data

Coxon, Philip
    The world of an island.
    1. Zoology—Scotland—North Uist
    I. Title   II. Coxon, Michele
    591.9′4114   QL259

    ISBN 0-571-10999-3

Contents

Contents

Illustrations

DRAWINGS

Illustrations

MAPS

Introduction: A View of the Island

North Uist is one of a chain of islands known as the Outer Hebrides, or Western Isles, which lie off the north-western coast of Scotland. The chain is about 240 miles (386 km) long, and from north to south the main islands are: Lewis and Harris (one island); North Uist; Benbecula; South Uist; Eriskay; Barra; and Mingulay. These islands are the most westerly part of Scotland, lying like a barrier protecting the mainland from the open Atlantic.

The Outer Hebrides, with their numerous subsidiary islands and remote western outliers, are among the most exposed areas in Europe. From their western coasts the Atlantic stretches unbroken towards America, while their eastern sea-board is separated from mainland Scotland by the Minch, in which the Inner Hebridean islands lie scattered and magical.

North Uist is roughly circular, with a diameter of about eighteen miles. It is separated from Harris to the north by a shallow channel called the Sound of Harris, and by tidal sand-flats from Benbecula to the south. It lies about 30 miles (48 km) west of Skye. Like Benbecula, North Uist is low-lying; its highest hill is Eaval, 1139 ft (347 m), which stands isolated in the south-east of the island and is an excellent point from which to examine the main physical features.

From the top of Eaval, the most impressive feature of North Uist is undoubtedly the amount of water it includes. Northwards from our hill stretches a wide level of bog seamed with cracks and gullies called peat-hags, interspersed with countless tidal inlets and freshwater lochs. Large, elaborately shaped lochs with peninsulas and islands; small lochans, like eyes in the moor; tidal lochs with skirts of brown seaweed; sandy flats; peat-

1. Looking down over central North Uist from the summit of Eaval

hags; hummocks and hills—all combine in central North Uist to present an aspect of such watery complexity that one is inclined to be lost in wonder at it all, rather than take a map and try to isolate significant patterns.

It is perhaps enough—certainly for anyone with no experience of Gaelic place-names—to separate the seawater inlets and tidal areas from the freshwater lochs. The sea-lochs have their mouths on the eastern coast and fall into two distinct groups: that of Locheport, close to the north of Eaval, cutting like a narrow knife-blade almost from coast to coast; and north again, the broader harbour of Lochmaddy with its maze of tidal inlets.

Tidal flats are stretches of offshore sand exposed at low tide, and they can be detected from the top of Eaval even when the tide is in, for the sea above them appears pale because of the white sand it shallowly covers. At high tide and in sunshine, these sand-based shallows are blends and gradations of colours: green through turquoise to deeper and deeper blue—an attractive feature of North Uist scenery. Such tidal flats separate North Uist from

Benbecula, and also occur extensively in the northern bays of Vallay and Vallaquie.

Freshwater lochs are numerous and, because the land is low-lying and comparatively flat, there are no long stretches of stream or river. This means that North Uist is less important for salmon fishing than other islands, and there are no streamside birds such as dippers and grey wagtails, which are widespread elsewhere in Highland Scotland.

The hills of North Uist achieve ruggedness only in Eaval and a similar hill-group, the Lees, a little to the north. Otherwise they form a low, ignoble rim around the central loch area. So, on the whole, North Uist is a great

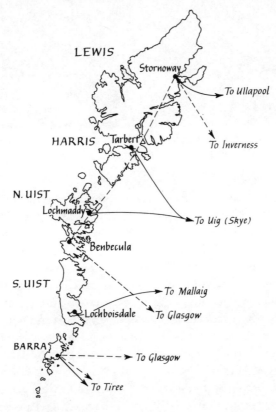

1. Air and sea connections between the Outer Hebrides and the mainland of Scotland

2. An island 'dun' on a freshwater loch. Note the causeway connecting the 'dun' with the shore of the loch

bowl of watery desolation — with a strong appeal to a minority of people who appreciate wild, solitary places, but perhaps haunting in quality rather than conventionally attractive or picturesque.

In direct contrast to the inland moors, the other distinctive feature of North Uist is the broad belt of flat, intensely green land running the length of the island on its western side. This is called the 'machair', a fertile grassland which occurs along the western coasts of all Outer Hebridean islands, but nowhere more extensively than in North and South Uist. From Eaval it is clearly seen that in North Uist the main belt of machair is broken into three areas. From north to south they are: the croftland of Balranald and Paible; the island of Kirkibost; and the island of Baleshare. Kirkibost and Baleshare are separated from each other and mainland North Uist by tidal sand-flats. Along the western side of the machairs runs a strip of white beach on which the Atlantic breaks its own white, endlessly.

3. A sea-cave in Lewisean gneiss, Griminish Point

It is immediately apparent that the population of North Uist is almost exclusively confined to this western machair. From Eaval, the only settlement visible on the eastern coast is the small town of Lochmaddy, in grand isolation round its harbour. But the western coast is dotted with houses, and marks of cultivation across the machair are easily discernible. Across the centre of the island one can see fragments of more machair-land fronting the Sound of Harris to the north, and here too it is comparatively densely populated and cultivated.

Once the broad physical contrasts have been noticed, they of course provoke questions. The western side of the island is obviously more exposed to weathering and battering by the Atlantic than the east coast, where the waters of the Minch are sheltered and darkly tranquil. So why do all the people live on the western side? What is this 'machair', and what curious quality does it have to encourage settlement and cultivation? And also, what is the reason for the comparative treelessness of North Uist? On the way up Eaval, one notices scrubby rowans and aspens growing on loch banks and islands but not elsewhere on the moors, and so far as one can see from here, the machair is completely treeless.

This book offers an explanation of these physical features, and attempts to give some account of the connection between them and the life which the island supports, both wild and human. Most important of all, it will enlarge on the significance of that stretch of water which makes North Uist the island world it is, fascinating and unique.

1. The Making of the Island

Geology

To provide reasons for North Uist's distinctive appearance, we must discuss the nature of the rock of which the island is made, and the processes by which it has been shaped into its present form. This involves going back almost to the very beginnings of geological time, for the rock of which North Uist is made is among the oldest known to man.

It is thought that the Earth is about 4,500,000,000 years old. The rock of which much of the Outer Hebrides, including North Uist, is formed, is known as Archaean or Lewisean Gneiss, and is about 3000,000,000 years old. It is volcanic in origin, and in its history has been liquefied by heat and pressure, cooled, folded, submerged under the sea and carved by ice and water. The gneiss may be inspected at Griminish Point in the north-west corner of the island, where the folds of pink and grey rock are washed clean by the Atlantic, and contain sparkles of quartz and mica. The low sea-cliffs along the east coast of the island are more sheltered and support more vegetation. In places no folds are visible and the rock drops black and smooth into the sea.

The Hebrides were once the western rim of a huge land-mass which included Europe, Iceland and Greenland. This land sank under the sea, and then reappeared as a mighty mountain range—the Caledonian Mountains. The folds of the Caledonian range ran from north-west to south-east, and are responsible for the alignment of the Hebrides as we know them today.

The Caledonian Mountains were formed about 500,000,000 years ago, and for hundreds of millions of years were subjected to such weathering that they were reduced to a low table-land. Elsewhere in Scotland and the Inner

Hebrides some of the sedimentary rocks which were deposited before the Caledonian upfolding survive as mountains above the floor of gneiss—the Torridonian Sandstone mountains of north-west Scotland are an example —but that part of the land which now forms the Outer Hebrides was weathered so much that all the surface rocks disappeared and only the table-land of gneiss remained.

The gneiss of which North Uist and Benbecula is made is older in origin than that of the other Hebridean islands, and was unaffected by the subsequent volcanic activity which caused the mountains of South Uist and Harris to be formed to south and north of our island.

The table-land of gneiss was raised by earth movements when it was still connected to the Continental Shelf, which reached as far west as St. Kilda and to Scandinavia in the east. Not until about 15,000,000 years ago did the flooding occur which cut off Scotland from Scandinavia by the North Sea and the Hebrides from mainland Scotland by the Minch.

North Uist was then part of an island mass which included all the Outer Hebrides. Not until the Ice Age, which began about 600,000 years ago, did the islands become separated.

There have been four main Ice Ages, and during the latest of these the whole of Northern Europe was covered in ice. The movement of the ice, especially at times of advance and retreat, deepened the existing river channels, scraped the rock bare, and cut the hills of North Uist into the shapes we see today. Where pockets of ice remained, holes were gouged in the gneiss to become the freshwater-loch complex in the centre of the island.

As the ice melted, the sea-level rose and flooded into valleys cut by the glaciers. The indented coastline of North Uist is, in fact, a series of valleys flooded at the same time as the islands were separated from each other by rising water. Today only the summits of the mountains remain, above the sea that flooded them during the retreat of the ice.

The machair of North Uist is a comparatively recent development, a feature of the interglacial period in which we live. As described in the introductory chapter, it is a belt of grassy, fertile land fringing the barren mass of the island on its western side.

Imagine North Uist as it was at the end of the last Ice Age, a scraped landscape of rock and heather, shelving into the sea. On the eastern side of the island lay the fairly sheltered Minch, but on the western side the

4. Shell-sand beach, western North Uist

Atlantic, pounding on to the shores. We are all familiar with sandy seashores, and you may have noticed that the sand of any area bears a relation to the rock of which the area is made. In Red Sandstone areas the sand is red-brown, in granite areas it may be white or golden, comprising fragments of the local rock. The open Atlantic off the western shores of the Outer Hebrides holds little rock in suspension — what it does hold is a 'dust' of organic material, skeletons of tiny vertebrates, shells, and microscopically small remains of such material, pounded and ground by pressure and abrasion.

This material is thrown on to the land by the sea, and is sand. So the sand of the Outer Hebrides, containing a high proportion of shell to rock, is 'shell-sand', white in colour, fine in texture.

This shell-sand, deposited along the western shores of North Uist as a series of magnificent beaches, is then blown inland by the prevailing westerly winds, and forms a belt of machair. The machair extends as far as

5. Weather: showers over the moorland

the influence of the sand. Why the machair should be fertile and support a great variety of wildlife will be explained in later chapters.

Climate

We have discussed the rock of which North Uist is made and the sand which is blown up on to the rock along the western shores. These are the foundations on which life builds, and to a certain extent they dictate the type of flora and fauna which will be present.

The third major factor influencing life is climate. Certain life-forms occur in certain geological situations, given certain climatic conditions. North Uist is wet, coolly temperate, and very windy. The coast is affected by the warm Gulf Stream and the winds passing over it, which keep the climate mild in winter and cool in summer. Hot days are rare in summer, frost and snow are rare in winter. Rainfall is not exceptionally high; warm air approaching the coast of North Uist does not immediately meet mountains which would cause condensation and precipitation. The land is flat, so rain, as it were, passes over. It is quite common to stand in dry conditions on the machair and watch rain veils obscure the mountains of South Uist and build up over the mountains of Skye to the east. Western Highland and Island mountains may have a rainfall in excess of 100 inches (254 cm) per annum; but the western machair of Uist can have as little as 30 to 40 inches (75–100 cm) a year.

It has been said that living in the Outer Hebrides is like living on the deck of a ship and this is most appropriate: seas on either side and wind sweeping the planks. No significant land-mass shelters North Uist, or the other Outer Hebridean islands, from westerly winds. They sweep straight off the Atlantic and scour the interior landscape mercilessly. The impression is not of exceptionally *strong* winds, though gale force winds blow for approximately a third of every winter. The most significant thing is that wind is *always* there. Summer and winter, there is always a noticeable wind, usually off the sea and of measurable strength.

The acid moor

The rock of which North Uist is made and the prevailing climatic conditions are perfect for the formation of various types of peat-bog. The land is flat, the rock is impermeable, i.e. the water does not soak into it as it does into limestone or chalk. Cool, cloudy conditions reduce evaporation so that although North Uist does not suffer a high rainfall, it is still a 'wet' island. Humidity is high because of the geology, geographical location and land-form.

Vegetation decays because of the action of micro-bacteria which feed on the organic matter, decomposing it. Gneiss is acidic, and the vegetation growing on it comprises mainly sour bog-mosses, sedges, heather and grasses. The acid plants grow more quickly than they can decay in the waterlogged conditions, so instead of breaking down into humus or soil, they form deepening layers of peat. Peat is therefore highly acidic and made up of waterlogged vegetative matter.

Central North Uist contains examples of each of the main types of peat bog: basin bog, raised bog and blanket bog. Basin bog is a result of poor drainage, and occurs where water collects and stagnates and is invaded by the bog moss, sphagnum. The bog forms in the depression where the water has lain. If conditions are such that peat formation can continue above the level of the depression, then the bog which forms above the basin bog is called raised bog. Blanket bog relies entirely on cold and humidity and forms over wide areas—a smooth 'blanket' of peat, level in aspect, sometimes seamed with peat-hags. The main vegetational cover in central North Uist comprises sphagnum, moor grass, and sedges, including cotton-grass. Ling (*Calluna*) and bell (*Erica*) heathers are present, but except on the better drained hillslopes they are sparse and dominated by grass and sedge.

Walk into the central moor area anywhere off the road from Lochmaddy to Clachan and you will instantly be aware of the essential character of the place. The ground is soft, your feet sink into the mat of moss and grass. Even in dry weather you will have difficulty in walking because of the eiderdown texture of the moor, but in winter, or after heavy rain, the moss is

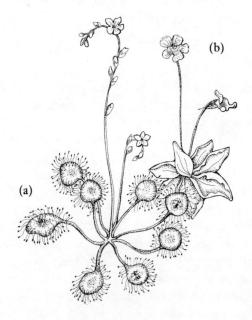

Fig. 1a Sundew (*Drosera rotundifolia*)
Fig. 1b Common butterwort (*Pinguicule vulgaris*)

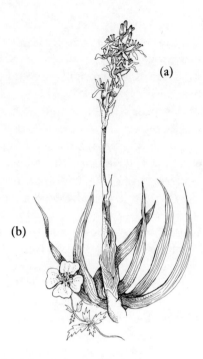

(a)

(b)

Fig. 2a Bog asphodel (*Narthecium ossifragum*)
Fig. 2b Tormentil (*Potentilla erecta*)

waterlogged and the moor is like a vast saturated sponge. The plants on the
moor are specially adapted to withstand such conditions—you may come
across the insectivorous sundew (*Drosera rotundifolia*), or butterwort
(*Pinguicule vulgaris*), both of which are common. These plants are able to
live in the poor ground because they are not wholly dependent on nutrients
from the soil; both are able to catch small insects on their leaves and secrete
digestive enzymes to break down their prey. The sundew has round, reddish
leaves with long surface 'hairs', each 'hair' having a sticky droplet on its end.
Flies or other small creatures become stuck on the hairs as if to fly-paper,
when their struggles trigger off a mechanical folding of the leaf and they are
trapped. The sundew may be one of two species—round or oval leaved—
and the plant has a single white flower. The butterwort has yellowish leaves
in a star pattern, with generally sticky upper surfaces; when the victim

becomes stuck to the leaf its outer edges curl inwards and the creature is
trapped and digested. The butterwort has a pretty violet-coloured flower on
a long stem. These insectivorous plants can survive in the wettest, most acid
situations—sundew often grows on sphagnum and butterwort on the
thinnest film of vegetation over naked rock.

Other common flowering plants of the central moor are bog asphodel
(*Narthecium ossifragum*), lousewort (*Pedicularis sylvatica*), and in outcrop
areas where the grass is a little sweeter and inaccessible to sheep and deer,
you may find tormentil (*Potentilla erecta*), St. John's wort (*Hypericum
humifusum*), milkwort (*Polygala vulgaris*), and even, in a few places, that
delicate little flower more characteristic of Highland woods, the wood sorrel
(*Oxalis acetosella*).

Wind and high acidity inhibit tree-growth, but climatic factors are not the
only reasons for North Uist's comparative treelessness. Pollen remains and
old stumps in the peat indicate that tree-growth was once more widespread,
and even now in sheltered areas and in places inaccessible to grazing
animals, dwarfed examples of such trees as hazel, aspen, rowan, juniper and
birch can be found. Willows of various species also occur.

The larger moorland lochs are too exposed to support much vegetation,
and their beds are mainly of naked rock—but in quieter inlets where peat is
deposited, and in tiny moorland lochans, deep and black, grow plants like
white or yellow water-lilies (*Nymphaea alba* and *Nuphar lutea*), water
lobelias (*Lobelia dortmanna*), bogbean (*Menyanthes trifoliata*) and flote-grass
(*Glyceria fluitans*).

The machair

The glory of North Uist, the feature which must more than any other
impress visitors, is its beaches. Along the western and part of the northern
coasts lie stretches of white sand backed by dunes and distinctive machair.
The shell-sand beaches are occasionally unbroken for up to two miles, as at
Traigh Iar (the long beach) on the western side of Baleshare, and the beach
of the same name off Sollas machair, in the north of the island. Sometimes
the beaches are indented into broadly curving bays, such as those at
Balranald, where a rocky headland pushes itself westward between deep
indentations, and Scolpaig, where a tiny and most picturesque beach lies
between sea-cliffs to the south and the headland of Griminish Point to the

6. Waterlilies (*Nymphaea alba*) in a loch

north. The seas to the west and north of North Uist are shallow and the tides may recede over vast level sand-flats.

We have already seen that the sand of which the beaches are made is shell-sand, i.e. the proportion of organic calcareous matter in the sand is high. The shell content of western island beaches ranges from twenty to eighty per cent of the total.

The peat-land of post-glacial North Uist shelves shallowly down towards the sea with its vast loads of shell-sand in suspension. The sand, which is fine, loose and light, is deposited by the sea, picked up by the prevailing westerly winds, which blow with a strength and consistency unknown elsewhere in the British Isles, and carried far inland on to the seaward slopes.

One can learn much about the formation of machair by walking in a direct line inland from any of the beaches and noting the changes in vegetation. The beach immediately above the high-tide line is barren—the sand is too unstable to allow any vegetative growth, and where excessive wind-scouring has occurred there may be stretches of shingle, the most lifeless coastal habitat of all. On the seaward faces of the coastal dunes there may be communities of plant life specially adapted to withstand the extreme conditions. Orache (*Atriplex patula*), sea rocket (*Cakile maritima*) and sea sandwort (*Arenaria peploides*) have fleshy leaves, so transpiration is reduced

7. Sea rocket growing on a beach

8. A track across the machair. Note erosion of the sandy soil

and the plants are able to withstand battering by dry salty winds. Silverweed (*Potentilla anserina*) is prostrate, creeping on long runners over sand and shingle. On sea-cliffs and other coastal areas, masses of sea pinks or thrift (*Armeria maritima*) make a splendid show in early summer.

Loose sand is transformed to stable machair only through the stabilising influence of marram-grass (*Ammophila arenaria*), a stiff-leaved, prickly bent which grows on dunes. Marram is able to withstand the dry, salty winds by allowing its leaves to curl up in dry conditions, reducing surface area and transpiration. Its stiff leaves resist grazing by sheep and rabbits and will grow through drifts of sand if they are buried. The long thready roots of marram-grass bind the sand and stop it blowing, and behind each of North Uist's beaches is a belt of dune supporting little vegetation other than marram-grass. When formed the belt of marram is a barrier to wind-blown sand and its protective influence is crucial to the existence of a stable, cultivable machair.

Gradually the marram becomes less common and is replaced further inland by a ground-cover of machair grass and flowers. Leguminous flowers such as clovers, vetches and trefoils are common, and by converting nitrogen in the air to nitrogenous compounds in the soil, they help to create conditions where an immensely rich flora can survive.

The calcareous sand blown inland from the beaches assists the breakdown of acid peat to give sweeter soil. Heather and sedges and the moor-grasses of the interior give way to the sweet green of the machair grasses, so the contrast of the brown moor and the green machair is entirely due to the influence of blown sand. Occasionally crofters extend the natural process by carting loads of sand from the beaches and dumping them on the moor, killing off the heather and improving the grazing for cattle and sheep.

The essential atmosphere of the summer machair is one of lightness, spaciousness and colour. The levels of the machair are riotous with more than eighty species of flowering plants, fragrant with scent of clover and thyme. Horizons are wide, the beaches curve white against the Atlantic; and in contrast to the uninhabited moorland, there are numerous crofts.

9. Pasture and loch

2. Wildlife

North Uist is one of the most fertile areas of Highland Scotland, and therefore supports a very rich and varied wildlife. In a book of this size and scope it is possible to mention only a few of the more conspicuous features, and to give information about those which the interested non-specialist is most likely to see.

The birds of North Uist

North Uist is becoming increasingly well-known as a bird-watching centre, and a large number of the island's visitors come for this purpose. The rich coastal grassland, coastal and moorland marshes, beaches, and tidal inlets provide a variety of habitats attractive to both migratory and breeding species.

BREEDING BIRDS OF THE MACHAIR

Perhaps the most obvious feature of machair birdlife is the density of breeding birds it supports. The breeding habitats are surprisingly various: coastal sand and shingle, sea-cliff and rocky headlands, cultivated grassland, rough pasture, and lime-rich lochs and marshes.

The beaches are exposed and often subject to much sand-blowing in the windy conditions, and few birds can breed here. Typical among species using the bare sand or shingle between high tide lines and the bases of the dunes are oystercatchers (*Haematopus ostralegus*), ringed plovers (*Charadrius hiaticula*), arctic terns (*Sterna paradisea*) and little terns (*Sterna albifrons*). The oystercatcher is one of our larger and more brightly coloured resident waders, unmistakable in its black and white plumage with red bill, legs and eyes. Its strong straight bill enables it to probe deeply into hard sand or mud for worms, to chisel limpets and barnacles off the rocks, or to break open mussels and cockles. It is a highly successful breeding species and is adaptable in its nesting requirements. It may nest on bare sand or

2. Physical features of North Uist

10. Bird-watching in a machair marsh

shingle, or quite often, and especially in Scotland, on inland pastures, where it favours smooth green sward. The oystercatcher's plumage camouflages the bird well while it sits on eggs among shingle, but it is ridiculously conspicuous against a background of grass.

The ringed plover is typically a bird of shore-line gravel and sand, and elsewhere in Britain it nests almost exclusively in such habitat. In North Uist, however, the beach environment is so hostile that ringed plovers frequently nest far from the sea, on the machair or even on stony patches near lochs. It is interesting to note that when ringed plovers elect to nest on machair, they often choose that state of machair which approximates most closely to beach conditions. First-year fallow, sandy and with a thin vegetative mesh of clover, wild pansy, silverweed and trefoil, suits them perfectly; and when the grass grows a little in May, it gives the very vulnerable chicks some useful cover.

Terns in Britain are very threatened species. Arctic and little terns nest in colonies on beaches, and in most areas in our over-populated country, beaches are continually disturbed by people during the summer months. The terns are kept from their eggs or chicks, which are eaten by gulls and other predators. The little tern, a fairylike, graceful bird, has unfortunately become so rare in Britain generally that it is included among the 'schedule

Fig. 3a Oystercatcher (*Haematopus ostralagus*)
Fig. 3b Ringed plover (*Charadrius liaticula*)

one' species — i.e. it is afforded special protection in the breeding season, and it is illegal for anyone to photograph or otherwise wilfully disturb these birds on or near their nests. But arctic terns are quite common in North Uist, with small colonies well distributed along the coasts, and little terns are not rare; there may be over a hundred nesting pairs in North Uist, and because they are comparatively unmolested, they have fair success. Both species of tern may nest on the beaches, and the arctic tern may lay its small olive eggs directly on bare sand, without any attempt to make more of a nest than a slight hollow moulded under its body. The little tern prefers fine shingle, and pairs may be found nesting among colonies of arctic terns if the habitat is right. In North Uist, however, both birds increase their chances of success by sometimes colonising machair areas; occasionally they will nest among growing corn, and as the corn grows rapidly in early summer, the chicks are concealed from predators and protected from the weather. Nesting in cornfields does have its disadvantages, however; I have seen eggs deserted as corn-strips have been fertilised by hand, and once a colony which I had under observation lost ten clutches when the area was sprayed with weedkiller from a tractor.

As the beaches of Britain become more polluted, are taken over for development of one kind or another, or are used by more people, the beach-breeding species inevitably become rarer. It is quite possible that the comparatively unthreatened and unused beaches of North Uist may before long support significant proportions of breeding species such as ringed plovers and terns.

The machair itself is intensely cultivated, but it does hold large numbers of skylarks (*Alauda arvensis*)—in spring the machair sky is a panoply of skylark song—and it is one of Britain's main areas for corn-buntings (*Emberiza calandra*). Corn-buntings are often regarded as dull brown birds, but here, where there is less bird song than elsewhere, the dry shivery call of the nesting bunting is very welcome. They sit on posts, fences and tussocks to sing, and when they nest near buildings (as they often do), they may choose chimney-pots or rooftrees as singing perches. Corn-buntings have two interesting habits: they dangle their legs when they fly, and they are polygamous; the single male singing on the rooftree may have two or three mates sitting on eggs in grass tussocks nearby.

Fig. 4 Corn-bunting (*Emberiza calandra*)

11. Camouflage: lapwing chick and marsh marigold

The machair marsh and loch systems afford splendid habitats for breeding birds. The marsh-edges with tussocks of sedge and rushes are excellent for nesting waders, the rough wet fields hold large numbers of lapwings (*Vanellus vanellus*) and gulls, and the loch edges with thick aquatic vegetation encourage ducks and rails. Mute swans, which winter in large numbers on Loch Bee in South Uist and Loch an Duin in North Uist, disperse in spring and breed very successfully on many moorland and most machair lochs.

Breeding waders in the marshes and pastures are really most spectacular. Lapwings are probably the most numerous species, laying their four eggs in late March and often having three clutches in a season. From May to mid-

July, the marshes teem with lapwing chicks, and one of the first signs of any predator in the area is the clouds of distressed lapwings wheeling about and crying. Redshanks (*Tringa totanus*) are almost as common, but while lapwings nest in open situations, redshanks usually use tussocks of rush and their nests may be difficult to locate. The song-flight of the redshank is most attractive; the bird flies in rough circles, piping clearly and rhythmically, then slowly descends, still piping, until it touches gracefully down with wings extended.

Snipe (*Gallinago gallinago*) nest in similar situations to redshanks and have a most unusual breeding display. They 'drum', i.e., flying at height they arrow downwards, letting their extended tail-feathers vibrate audibly in the air current. They may also fly jerkily around giving low ticking calls, rather like loud airborne clocks.

Fig. 5a Redshank (*Tringa totanus*)
Fig. 5b Lapwing (*Vanellus vanellus*)

(a)

(b)

Fig. 6a Dunlin (*Calidris alpina*)
Fig. 6b Snipe (*Gallinago gallinago*)

Another typical wader of the machair is the dunlin (*Calidris alpina*). In Britain, dunlins are regarded mainly as wintering birds, and most bird-watchers are familiar with them as small birds of estuary and fresh wetland, where they may congregate in huge wintering flocks. As a breeding species, however, they are less familiar, and in mainland Britain they are mainly restricted to northern upland habitat, where they breed on moorland, usually by lochs or tarns in pairs or small colonies. Machair marshes, however, support large breeding populations, and pairs are generally distributed in loose colonies. They prefer marsh-edges, especially if grazed by cattle so that the vegetation is short and the ground soft and churned into hoof-prints and hummocks. In this situation the nest is often made in an old hoof-print. Dunlins' eggs are slightly smaller than snipes' eggs and often darker in colour, but the main distinguishing feature is the way the brown blotches are in oblique whorls across the dark olive background.

In the breeding season, dunlins are transformed from rather dull, grey waders into one of our most appealing machair species. Their backs become rich ruddy-brown flecked with black, and they develop a black patch on their white bellies. Their call, too, is evocative: a rising trill reminiscent of the winter call, but more prolonged and musical.

Machair marshes are the breeding habitat for one of Britain's rarest waders, the red-necked phalarope (*Phalaropus lobatus*). This tiny, delicate bird nests quite numerously in latitudes north of Britain, but the few British pairs are at the extreme southern fringe of the breeding range for this species, and numbers, never large, have declined drastically in the last half-century or so. There is now a maximum of two pairs nesting annually in

Fig. 7 Red-necked phalarope (*Phalaropus lobatus*) and bogbean (*Menyanthes trifoliata*)

North Uist, in a maximum of two locations; and probably no more than half a dozen pairs breed in the Outer Hebrides.

It may be said that phalaropes within their main breeding range are common enough, and as far as world numbers are concerned, the survival or disappearance of the British population is insignificant. On the other hand, the phalaropes are so charming in appearance and unique in habit that their extinction in any area is an aesthetic loss.

The most obviously unusual thing about phalaropes is that, although wader-shaped, they swim almost like ducks. Their feet are not webbed, but they have flaps of skin, called 'lobes', attached to their toes, enabling them to swim buoyantly and quickly in the shallow lochs which they prefer. Sometimes they may swim or 'spin' in close circles on the water; it may be both a courting display and a means of agitating the loch vegetation and silty bottom, bringing the tiny creatures on which they feed to the surface. 'Spinning' apart, the action of the phalarope is always quite unmistakable; they move jerkily, with a fairylike delicacy picking at the surface of the water or craning to take food from rushes or other waterplants.

Phalaropes are also unusual in that the roles of the sexes at breeding time are largely reversed. The female, with her deeply red neck, contrasting white and black body plumage and neat white facial patch, is the more brightly coloured of the pair. She takes the initiative in display and courtship, and drives off intruders on her territory. The male, which has similar but less vivid plumage, incubates the eggs and tends the young.

Phalaropes arrive at their breeding stations in late May or early June, and are gone by mid-August. So they are sitting on eggs or tending small, vulnerable young in July or early August, the months when most holidaymakers, including naturalists and bird-watchers, are about. Anyone who comes to North Uist with the intention of seeing phalaropes should bear in mind that this is a very rare, in fact almost extinct, species. As such it is illegal for anyone without a licence wilfully to disturb the birds at their breeding places, for photography, observation, or any other reason. Phalaropes are notoriously tame; they will swim around at the water's edge only inches from the feet of an observer, but this does not mean that they are not distressed, and in fact such confiding behaviour makes them very vulnerable. Clutches and young have to my knowledge been crushed by negligent bird-watchers and photographers. Anyone who wishes to see phalaropes should contact the warden of Balranald R.S.P.B. Reserve before setting out to look for them. He will know whether it is possible, or advisable, for visitors to see phalaropes, according to the condition of the season.

The Outer Hebrides are one of the few remaining breeding stations in Britain for that remarkable game bird, the corncrake (*Crex crex*). It was once common throughout Britain, but its numbers decreased, partly because of its habit of nesting in cornfields. While farming methods were less mechanised and intensive, the corncrakes survived, but with the disappearance of hedgeside banks and other rough unharvestable places, corncrakes quickly became extinct in most English, Welsh, and lowland Scottish counties. In the Outer Hebrides harvests are late enough to allow

Fig. 8 Corncrake (*Crex crex*) and iris

the corncrakes to fledge their young safely before cutting, and there is a great deal of rough uncultivable ground where they may breed undisturbed.

The machair of North Uist is well populated with corncrakes. Their call, or song, is the most distinctive thing about them—a grating, rasping noise which simply goes on and on, endlessly. It is one of the characteristic sounds of summer evening on the machair, and so long as you are not trying to get to sleep at the time it can be pleasing to the ear. They will call during the day, especially early in the season while they are establishing territories, but early morning and late evening, the prolonged summer twilight of those northern latitudes, are the times when they are generally most vocal. During one spring and summer I lived in a caravan on the machair of North Uist, and a pair of corncrakes soon found that they could creep underneath and shelter there from the rain. I didn't begrudge them their shelter, and I much appreciated being able to watch them at close quarters as they poked around outside—but when they stole under the caravan at night and the male began to crake, crake, I used to lie sleeplessly and wish them elsewhere!

Corncrakes are shaped like very slim partridges, are reddish-brown in colour and are difficult to see as they creep around in corn or long grass. They are most readily seen soon after they arrive in May. Although they don't call much if it is cold, the vegetation is short and they can often be seen scuttling for cover from one sprouting iris-clump to the next. I have found that in early summer corncrakes inhabit marsh edges, where the vegetation is longest at that time, and more nest in the marshes than in the machair cornfields. When the young are hatched, however, the families move into the growing corn or into nettle-beds around the crofts and, except for an occasional bird flying low over the corn, they are rarely seen. Corncrakes don't fly much, and when they do, they are clumsy and weak on the wing. It is hardly surprising that the people of the machair once refused to believe that such birds could migrate, and thought instead that the skulking corncrake turned into a rat during the winter.

BIRD MIGRATION

In addition to providing excellent breeding habitat, the machair is also of prime importance to birds on migration. Birds tend to follow coasts, and as the west coast of the Hebrides is the most westerly land in Britain, vast numbers of birds use the machair and the beaches as a sort of 'corridor' in spring on their way to breeding-grounds in Iceland, Greenland, Scandinavia and all stations north, and in autumn when returning southwards after breeding.

April and May are the main months of the spring migration. Redwings (*Turdus pilaris*), thrush-like birds, go by in huge flocks, usually following the sheltered eastern edge of the machair. Lapwings and oystercatchers also go over, often at night, but the migration scene is at its most active along the beaches, where north-bound waders have a long narrow strip of comparatively rich feeding along which to congregate and travel. The shell-sand itself may not be specially rich in invertebrate food, but what makes the beaches so popular with birds is the immense amounts of seaweed thrown up by high tides and winter storms. As the banks of seaweed, often several feet deep, begin to decay, they become infested by insects which breed and feed there. The decomposition process generates heat and in a frozen March I have broken open a bank of seaweed to find the decomposing matter soft and warm under the icy crust, teeming with flies and maggots and studded with tiny eggs. The seaweed tends to build up in sheltered bay corners and rocky areas, and here the migratory birds can congregate in huge numbers.

It is an instructive pastime to sit among the low-tide rocks of a beach, and note the different habits of the waders feeding there. In the shallow water there may be bar-tailed godwits (*Limosa lapponica*), wading up to the knee-joints of their long legs and probing deeply with their long, slightly upturned bills. It is the length of their legs and bills which enables these birds to feed while actually standing in the water, so they are not dependent on seaweed or soft muddy sand to allow them to probe, and they are among the few waders which commonly feed on 'clean' beaches—i.e. without rocks or seaweed. Oystercatchers have long legs and bills and they too will feed on clean sand, although they often prefer to prise crustaceans off the rocks or feed on cockles in tidal inlets.

At the very edge of the waves are sanderlings (*Calidris alba*). Small waders, often in flocks of fifty or more, they are easily identifiable by their habit of following the waves as they swirl up and down the sand, picking minute particles from the foam. Rarely flying except to flip away from exceptionally large waves, the sanderlings run quickly and jerkily to and fro on their short black legs. In winter they are very white in appearance, like nothing more than the blobs of foam they feed on, but at times of migration

Fig. 9 Bar-tailed godwit (*Limosa lapponica*)

they may be in intermediate or full breeding plumage with more brown and chestnut on breast and back.

Ringed plovers are possibly the most numerous of all migratory waders to use North Uist's beaches. During the migration periods every beach holds hundreds of these appealing little birds, and it is suggested that the Hebrides contain a significant proportion of the total British population at this time. They will feed almost anywhere on the beach, and in muddy inlets, but they seem particularly to prefer the lines of high-tide seaweed.

Dunlin are often present with ringed plovers and, at times of dunlin migration, are almost as numerous. With their longer bills, they prefer softer ground than ringed plovers for feeding, and the greatest concentrations occur in areas of wet seaweed or on muddy tidal flats.

Turnstones (*Arenaria interpres*) are medium-sized plump waders with red legs, and they feed almost exclusively among rock pools and in the thickest deposits of tide-line seaweed. Some summer along the coasts of North Uist, but they have not yet been known to breed, and the largest numbers occur at times of migration. The summer plumage of the turnstone is an attractive tortoiseshell, which blends in well with the colour of the seaweed and seaweedy rocks on which they feed. Perhaps the most energetic of all tide-line feeders, turnstones do indeed overturn surprisingly large stones to get at food beneath, and they throw the seaweed around in much the same way as blackbirds rummaging through leaves.

Another wader with a very distinctive feeding action is the rarer greenshank (*Tringa nebularia*), a medium-large wader with whitish plumage and green legs. It runs about in wet mud or in sand-pools, furrowing through the water with its slightly upturned bill.

It is interesting to note that because the beaches of North Uist lie in the path of many migrating waders, and because of the food-rich seaweed, waders which usually prefer muddy estuarine conditions, such as dunlin and greenshank, and even birds usually associated with freshwater marsh like the uncommon ruff and black-tailed godwit (*Limosa limosa*), when they pass through North Uist, often feed quite untypically on the sandy beaches.

Of all the main migratory birds to use North Uist, none are more evocative of wilderness than the wild geese. From mid-March to early May each year, thousands of greylag geese (*Anser anser*), hundreds of whitefront

(b)

(a)

Fig. 10a Purple sandpiper (*Calidris maritima*)
Fig. 10b Turnstone (*Arenaria interpres*)

(a)

(b)

Fig. 11a Greylag goose (*Anser anser*)
Fig. 11b Barnacle goose (*Branta leucopsis*)

geese (*Anser albifrons*) and scores of pinkfeet geese (*Anser brachyrhyncus*) pass over, most of them en route for their breeding stations in Iceland and Greenland. Given a suitable day at the right time, the skeins are passing high and continuously, making their incomparably wild, musical calls. Many go over at night, and anyone out late may hear them passing and perhaps see dark wing-shapes against the stars.

The instinct to migrate is very strong, sometimes too urgent to allow the birds to wait for good weather conditions before flying north. Many geese may congregate on the marshes and machair of North Uist and feed quietly before undertaking the long overseas flight to Iceland; but eventually they go, and I have watched greylags and whooper swans (*Cygnus cygnus*) launching out north-westwards into the blackest of storms and furious headwinds, flying low and steadily out to sea until the birds were no longer visible and only their calls came blowing back on the wind.

Significantly large proportions of the world's population of barnacle

Fig. 12 Whooper swan
(*Cygnus cygnus*)

geese (*Branta leucopsis*) winter on the coasts of Scotland, and numbers of
these birds, probably the flocks from Islay, Barra and part of those from the
Solway, pass along the western shores of North Uist on migration to their
breeding grounds in northern Asia. If there are strong westerly winds (as
often happens in early spring) numbers of barnacle geese may land and rest
on the machair. This phenomenon usually happens in late April. On two
occasions I have been lucky enough to see over a thousand of these birds
accumulate on Balranald headland, in the north-western extremity of North
Uist. Barnacles are small 'black' geese with white facial patches and their
call, unlike that of the more musical grey geese, is high-pitched and yelping.

WINTERING BIRDS
The main coastal wintering habitats for birds are estuarine flats, saltings and
marshes. North Uist contains all these habitats, but none occupy large areas.
Tidal inlets are numerous but small, food-rich marshes are never more than

a few hundred acres and are confined to the machair area. These reasons and the fact that North Uist's winter climate is windy, wet and hostile, reduce the island's importance as a wintering area for most birds, and those that do winter here are in small scattered flocks rather than in the vast congregations typical of the larger English and east-coast estuary/marsh systems.

A flock of more than 2000 barnacle geese winters annually on the Monach islands off the west coast of North Uist. They arrive in October, and spend a mainly undisturbed winter feeding on the exceptionally rich machair. In spring, fishermen from Grimsay live on the Monachs and begin to fish for lobsters in the surrounding waters, and this disturbance no doubt combines with the migratory instinct, impelling the geese to leave.

The other islands off North Uist, and especially the green sheltered islands in the Sound of Harris, hold numbers of wintering greylag geese. The tidal inlets and marshes of Baleshare and Balranald also have small flocks, but it is uncertain whether these birds come in from the north; are

Fig. 13a Shoveler (*Anas clypeata*)
Fig. 13b Tufted duck (*Aythya fuligula*)

the breeding population from central North Uist; or are a mixture of the two.

The number of wildfowl in North Uist increases considerably from October to March. The breeding gadwall (*Anas strepera*) may migrate, but tufted ducks (*Aythya fuligula*), mallard (*Anas platyrhynchos*), shoveler (*Anas clypeata*), coots (*Fulica atra*), moorhens (*Gallinula chloropus*) and mute swans (*Cygnus olor*) remain to face the wind and rain, and they are joined by incoming populations of teal (*Anas crecca*), wigeon (*Anas penelope*) pochard (*Aythya ferina*), pintail (*Anas acuta*), and goldeneye (*Bucephala clangula*). Mallard, shoveler, pintail and teal are dabbling ducks—i.e. rather than dive for food they up-end in shallow water and sieve vegetation through their bills for edible matter. With coots and moorhens they inhabit the freshwater marshes, which are often enlarged by floods. Wigeon are grazing duck—they nip grass with their bills and move rather like sheep over short salting turf or grassy marsh-edges. They are present in small scattered flocks, but a flock of 1000 or more is said to winter annually in the elaborate system of tidal inlets and saltings round Lochportain in the north-east of the island.

Tufted ducks, pochard and goldeneye are diving ducks. They swim underwater and catch animal food—insects, crustaceans and small fish. They tend to congregate on the deeper locks along the machair-moor boundary, but if the weather becomes really cold they may move down to the machair lochs, and the goldeneye may take to the sea.

Mergansers (*Mergus serrator*) are another winter resident, numbers of which fish either in the bays or the freshwater marshes. These are 'sawbill' ducks—they have longish, narrow bills with backward-tending serrations enabling them to catch and hold the fish and eels on which they feed. If mergansers are numerous, they may be regarded as vermin by the owners of fishing rights or trout hatcheries, and their numbers accordingly reduced.

Although wind-scoured and seemingly inhospitable, the beaches of North Uist are used by wintering waders. Ringed plovers stay, as do numbers of sanderling, turnstones and oystercatchers. The purple sandpiper (*Calidris maritima*) (see Fig. 10) is exclusively a winter wader, arriving in October and leaving in April, feeding on the most seaward of coastal rocks. Plump and grey, they look rather mouse-like as they creep slowly about, hunching themselves up against the winds. Other wintering

Fig. 14 Golden plover (*Pluvialis apricaria*)

waders such as golden plover (*Pluvialis apricaria*), lapwings, redshanks and curlews (*Numenius arquata*), feed between the marshes and the tide-line, according to conditions of tide and weather. I have spent many a happy hour sprawled among tidal saltings at dusk, listening to curlews and redshanks flighting down to their roosting places on the low-tide sand-flats.

SEABIRDS
Many people visiting North Uist for the first time are surprised to find that the island has few sea-cliffs, and no real seabird colonies.

Fulmar petrels (*Fulmarus glacialis*) breed on what cliffs the island does have. Colonies are small and scattered, but in some places the fulmars nest in easily accessible situations on cliff-tops. In places where few people go, including some uninhabited islands, the fulmars even nest at ground level, on sand-dunes or in corners of derelict buildings.

A hundred years ago, fulmars bred only on St. Kilda, the famous oceanic island 40 miles (64 km) north-west of North Uist. The St. Kildans relied very much on the birds and their eggs for food, and it is possible that their annual hunting expeditions to the fulmar colonies kept the numbers in control. The people left St. Kilda in 1930, and even before that the St. Kildans had stopped culling the fulmars so regularly. This may have

contributed towards an increase in fulmar numbers, and it is suggested that
the birds also benefited from an easy food supply provided by the offal
thrown overboard from fishing boats.

Whatever the reason, the fulmars increased in numbers and extended
their breeding range with quite astonishing success. They now breed along
the coasts of Britain as far south as Kent in the east and Pembrokeshire in the
west. North Uist is the nearest major land mass to St. Kilda, and must have
been one of the first areas to be newly colonised when the fulmar population
began to expand.

Fulmars can be easily distinguished from seagulls by their habit of gliding
serenely about the cliffs, their short rudder-like wings held stiffly

(a)

(b)

Fig. 15a Fulmar (*Fulmarus glacialis*)
Fig. 15b Shag (*Phalacrocorax aristotelis*)

12. Herring gull eggs and chick

outstretched. They are quite confiding, and may come gliding in to hang only feet away from the observer's head, when the characteristically high-domed petrel profile, the tubular protuberances above the bill, and the strangely impassive dark eyes can be clearly seen. The single white eggs are laid in May, but the young birds stay on their ledges until mid-September. Abandoned by their parents some weeks earlier, the chicks lose weight until they are able to take to the wing and fend for themselves. Fulmars are mild, inoffensive-looking creatures, but I warn you that if you approach a chick or adult on the nest too closely, it will spray the contents of its crop at you — an evil-smelling fishy oil almost impossible to remove.

Shags (*Phalacrocorax aristotelis*) and cormorants (*Phalacrocorax carbo*) nest mainly on off-shore islands — cormorants on slabby shelving rocks, often in considerable colonies, shags in ones and twos on sea-cliffs. Both are regarded as vermin, and cormorants were once shot for eating and considered a delicacy. The largest cormorant colony in North Uist numbers about 180 pairs and is unusual in that it is situated on a low cliff above a freshwater loch about a mile from the nearest sea. Cormorants commonly fish in fresh water, but the smaller shags are exclusively seabirds.

Another bird which breeds in small numbers on the coastal rocks of North Uist is the black guillemot (*Cepphus grylle*) or 'tystie'. In summer the tystie is coal-black except for white patches on its wings, red eye-rings and red legs and feet. In winter it belies its name by turning almost white. It has a most unusual call—a thin plaintive wail which echoes piteously among the rocks where it breeds. Herring gulls (*Larus argentatus*) and great black-backed gulls (*Larus marinus*) breed along the cliff-tops and by rocky shores. A few great black-backs nest on islands or freshwater lochs. Lesser black-backed gulls (*Larus fuscus*) are summer residents, few in number, and usually nesting in colonies of other gulls. In other parts of Britain, these three species of gull have increased in number, feeding on man's domestic and industrial waste, and have become a real menace to the eggs and chicks of other birds. Although fiercely predatory in North Uist as elsewhere, these larger gulls have not increased in number enough to reduce other island species to any extent. Common gulls (*Larus canus*) and black-headed gulls

Fig. 16 Great black-backed gull (*Larus marinus*)

(*Larus ridibundus*) nest in large colonies, occasionally together, and while the black-headed gull is a mild-eyed eater of worms and insects, the common gull is very much a threat to other birds. Baleshare Island is a long sand-dune peninsula, and on it breed large numbers of common waders, a colony of arctic terns and one of the island's large colonies of little terns. There is also a colony of common gulls, and the gulls prey mercilessly on the eggs and young of the other birds, especially the smaller waders and the terns. Anyone walking through the area unavoidably causes the terns and waders to fly up and expose their eggs and young to the gulls—so much so that a research student working in the area one summer found that the only way to prevent destructive attacks by the gulls was to send someone to stand in the colony, and then work quickly while the gulls were all occupied with mobbing the intruder. I have seen common gulls decimate broods of mallard in Balranald marshes, bashing the chicks on stones and swallowing them whole—and a crofter friend of mine told me that he used to eat common gulls' eggs with relish, until one day his reaper blade killed a huge buck rat and a common gull came down and immediately swallowed it.

Shelduck (*Tadorna tadorna*) and eider-ducks (*Somateria mollissima*) are North Uist's commonest sea-ducks. I always think of them together, as both species bring their newly hatched young from the machair sand-dunes to the sheltered bays, and family parties of both species are often seen in close proximity. But the breeding and feeding habits of eider and shelduck actually differ considerably. Outside the breeding season, shelduck prefer to feed in tidal inlets, often on sand or mud-flats or among saltings, whereas eider are more oceanic, feeding in flocks and diving or dabbling round skerries and bays for crabs and small fish. Shelduck breed in sand-dunes, often in disused rabbit holes, and sometimes quite a little way from the sea. Eiders nest in the marram-grass or grass of sand-dunes and offshore islands, but their nest is on the ground, and consists of a rich bed of 'eider-down'— feathers plucked from the breast of the female bird. Like shelduck, eiders may nest away from the sea's edge, and when the young have hatched they are walked down to the waves for their first swim. Both species, but particularly eiders, tend their young in 'crèches', numbers of ducklings supervised by several adult birds. Male eiders tend to form separate flocks at this time, but shelduck pairs stay together. Mortality is very high among the young of both species. As the young are walked to the sea, and as they bob around in the bays, they are vulnerable to attack by predators, especially gulls, so that a gathering of thirty small ducklings may be systematically reduced to less than a dozen in a few days. Each species lays large clutches, up to thirteen or fourteen eggs, to compensate for such heavy losses among ducklings.

In July and August the visiting bird-watcher may be confused to find that all eider-ducks, male and female alike, are dark brown or mottled in colour, quite unlike the dapper illustrations in the bird books. All wildfowl at this time are moulting their feathers and can be difficult to identify unless you are familiar with their distinctive shapes and habits, or catch sight of the brightly coloured speculum feathers in the rear part of the upper wings

Fig. 17a Shelduck (*Tadorna tadorna*)
Fig. 17b Eider-duck (*Somateria mollissima*)

which are unaffected by the moult. Most shelduck, in fact, disappear from our coasts at this time and fly away to moult in huge flocks off the coast of Holland, not returning to our inlets and beaches until late autumn or early winter.

Fig. 18 Long-tailed duck (*Clangula hyemalis*)

Legend has it that long-tailed ducks were once human inhabitants of the island of Berneray, off the north coast of North Uist. These people were exclusively fishermen rather than crofters, and were turned into sea-ducks. The long-tailed ducks (*Clangula hyemalis*), little sea-ducks which appear off North Uist coast on migration and in winter, are the descendants of these people from Berneray. Watching a dozen long-tailed ducks loafing in a bay one fine May morning, listening to them crooning and splashing across the still water, I reflect that the fishermen of Berneray who underwent the change have very little to complain about!

Seabirds which nest in cliffs and live in colonies, such as gannets (*Sula bassana*), guillemots (*Uria aalge*), razorbills (*Alca torda*), puffins (*Fratercula arctica*) and kittiwakes (*Rissa tridactyla*) all appear off the coasts of mainland North Uist although none breed there. Razorbills are the most commonly seen species of auk, and during migration times parties can be seen flying by or resting on the water close inshore. Kittiwakes are usually immature birds from colonies on offshore islands, and gannets, numbers of which are always present, are probably all associated with the colonies on St. Kilda, the world's largest breeding station for this species. The gannets we see off the coast of North Uist may be non-breeding birds, or birds with young on St. Kilda using our waters for fishing. The forty miles between North Uist and St. Kilda is a very trivial distance for a commuting gannet. The first indication that shoals of fish are moving into North Uist bays is the parties of gannets which come to prey on them. One by one the gannets dive headlong into the water, often from a height of 30 or 40 feet (9 or 12 m). Sometimes they feed in this way in the shallowest waters, or among tidal rocks, but they never seem to misjudge the water's depth and they invariably bob up safely after the most dangerous of dives.

If strong westerly winds blow persistently in spring or autumn, droves of Manx shearwaters (*Puffinus puffinus*) may pass quite close to the shores of North Uist. These birds fly in a very distinctive way—in single file, very close to the water, often gliding along the wave-troughs and banking over the crests. As they turn, they show their black backs and white undersides alternately. While watching shearwaters, you may be lucky enough to see a storm petrel (*Hydrobates pelagicus*), a swallow-sized bird, black with a white rump, fluttering over the wave-crests. Both of these species belong to the petrel family and both nest in rocks of offshore islands. The best place for seeing them from the North Uist coast is the headland at Griminish Point, which gives good views over the flight-routes through the Sound of Harris.

MOORLAND BIRDS
The acid, comparatively barren and uniform habitat of the central moorlands supports its own unique wildlife. As far as birds are concerned, it is a breeding habitat only, being empty in winter, but the birds which do breed there are unusual and interesting. The following are only a few of the more typical species.

The peaty levels of the island's centre are used by arctic skuas which breed in loose colonies of up to four pairs. Arctic skuas (*Stercorarius parasiticus*), are hawk-like, about the size of herring gulls, but with powerful bodies and sharply pointed wings. In the breeding season, the adult birds of the species have long whippy tail-streamers. They vary in colour, some

Fig. 19a Arctic tern (*Sterna paradisea*)
Fig. 19b Arctic skua (*Stercorarius parasiticus*)

being a uniform sooty brown (called dark phase), some being completely white underneath (light phase) and others showing degrees of dark or lightness, often with conspicuous dark neck-bands across the throat.

Skuas are unusual in that they are almost entirely piratical in their feeding habits. Rarely catching food for themselves, they prefer to harry other birds, particularly terns, until they drop or disgorge food which the skuas may catch in mid-air. North Uist provides these birds with a vast area of suitable breeding habitat. They could breed almost anywhere across the island's interior—and yet wherever they choose to nest on the moors, they are never far from the coasts and machair where terns and other seabirds breed.

The skuas can be watched on the coast. They tend to appear with migrating terns, or they come in from the moors to chase the terns or waders. It is fascinating to see a skua select, say, an arctic tern carrying a fish, then chase it with terrific determination, following every movement of the tern with incredible speed. Sometimes they even seem to anticipate the tern's movements.

Skuas are late breeders, occupying their nesting territories from mid-May to mid-August, laying two, or occasionally three, eggs in the grass or heather. In courtship, or as they rise to harry intruders, they swing and circle around, and their wild, yelling calls match perfectly the desolation of their habitat.

The watery interior of North Uist makes it an ideal breeding place for red- and black-throated divers. Divers are goose-like birds specially adapted to diving and swimming underwater to catch fish. Outside the breeding season they frequent sea-coasts and open seas, but both species breed by moorland

Fig. 20 Black-throated diver (*Gavia arctica*)

freshwater. So adapted are they to swimming that neither species can walk. Their legs are positioned far back on the body to give maximum push for diving, but on land they can only slither awkwardly along on their bellies.

Red-throated divers (*Gavia stellata*) are the smaller of the two, and they breed on the shores of small lochans, which they leave to feed in the sea. Black-throated divers (*Gavia arctica*) tend to breed on islands of larger lochs and feed in the lochs where they breed. Both species are restricted in nesting habitat by their inability to walk—the eggs have to be laid at the water's edge, with only the most gradual slope to negotiate from eggs to water. A rise in water-levels can flood the nests; a drought can make it impossible for the diver to reach its eggs from the loch.

The best way to watch divers on North Uist is to sit quietly at any of the many places where freshwater lochs adjoin a road, and watch for the birds to come flighting over. They are a rare and wary species, and it is inadvisable to search out and visit their nests.

EAGLES

Golden eagles (*Aquila chrysaetos*), the largest birds of prey in Britain, are usually associated with the Scottish mainland landscape, where mountains are high and precipitous and there are fastnesses remote from roads and little disturbed by people. Compared to areas like these, the North Uist landscape is, as we have seen, low-lying and nowhere is beyond the reach of a comfortable day's walking. Nevertheless, North Uist supports a minimum of three, and a maximum of five, pairs of golden eagles each year.

Depending on weather conditions, eagles will begin nesting activity early in the year. Given a warm spell in January or February, they will begin repairing their nest-sites and indulging in courtship displays over their chosen cliff or outcrop. They mate for life, staying in pairs, often on their nesting territory, throughout the winter, and inside a territory of, say, 50 square miles (12,950 hectares), they will have two or three alternative breeding sites which they may use in regular rotation. Habits differ from pair to pair, however, and in North Uist I know of one pair which returns annually to the same site and has no alternative sites; in contrast to another pair which has a choice of three sites on one crag, and two more sites on another crag less than a hundred yards away.

Courtship involves soaring and tumbling on currents of warm air, sometimes thousands of feet above the hilltops. The massive wings—seven feet from tip to tip—bear the birds up easily and they seem to have delicate 'finger-tip' control of winds, enabling them to spiral elegantly or dive together, catching at each other with outstretched talons.

The first egg is usually laid towards the end of March and the hen eagle begins to incubate immediately. The clutch is usually of two eggs, but the second egg may not be laid until a week or so later. This system of 'staggered' laying and incubation is practised by other birds of prey and is very important to the natural regulation of numbers of the species to available food. In early May the eagle's first egg hatches and that chick is fed

Fig. 21 Golden eagle (*Aquila chrysaetos*)

and allowed to develop for up to a week before the second chick appears. So the eyrie now contains one well-fed, week-old chick, and one chick newly hatched and almost helpless. The hen eagle will not feed each eaglet in turn; she will tear the prey into strips and push it into whichever beak is thrust most strongly towards her at the time. So unless she can bring in enough food to satiate the first-hatched, stronger eaglet and have sufficient left over to satisfy the younger eaglet as well, the younger will be deprived and die of starvation. This, in fact, is what usually happens. The food supply for eagles in Scotland is such that there is rarely enough to satisfy both eaglets of a clutch, and in most cases only one eaglet survives. The dead eaglet is usually torn up and fed to the survivor. All of which may seem rather pitiless, but if more young eagles were produced than could be supported by the available food supply, then many more birds would suffer, and the overall numbers of the species would decline. The system of staggered incubation ensures that fledglings are as strong and capable as possible given the current prey situation, and that a maximum of young eagles survive to fly.

The eaglet stays in the eyrie until August. By then, its interior is, in human terms, a most unhygienic place. Fragments of uneaten meat and copious droppings from the chick litter the nest, which becomes fly-infested and maggoty, and smells quite appalling. During incubation, the male eagle brings food to the female, but when the eaglet is strong enough to be left, both adults will hunt, bringing food to the eyrie perhaps twice a day, at morning and evening. The adult birds may decorate the nests with sprigs of greenery, but the reason behind this curious behaviour is yet unknown—it certainly does very little to relieve the unpleasantness of a well-used nest interior!

In August the eaglet may make its first flight, usually a clumsy 'downhill' affair which may not carry it far from the nest. It may in fact be several weeks before the immature bird can take a place in the sky beside its parents. But there is still much to be learnt. The business of killing to eat is a difficult one, requiring perfect co-ordination of muscle and eye, and a knowledge of what prey can be taken and what is too large for the eagle to manage or too small to be worthwhile. This is a crucial time for an eaglet, and it is a sobering thought that in fact the majority of fledged eagles, in common with other birds of prey, just don't learn well or fast enough. When the eaglets are dismissed by the adults in October or November, many are unable to feed themselves, and die. This is another example of the way nature operates to ensure that those birds which do survive to perpetuate the species are as strong as possible.

The food supply for eagles in North Uist is probably plentiful when compared with eagle habitat in the mainland mountains. The machair holds a good population of small birds and rabbits, seabirds are numerous, especially at times of migration, and most important of all, mortality amongst sheep is very high, ensuring a good supply of carrion, on which eagles mainly feed. Other advantages are the comparative quiet of the moors and hills, which are unattractive to hillwalkers, and the fact that there is no intensive grouse-shooting, so that eagles are not persecuted by gamekeepers in the cause of 'sport'.

Despite the apparent advantages, breeding eagles in North Uist have very poor success. In 1973, out of five possible sites, four were occupied at the beginning of the season. One pair lost its eggs in April, another deserted a small chick because of disturbance by humans, the eggs of a third pair were infertile. The remaining pair reared one eaglet. In 1974, four sites were again occupied. The eggs from one site again disappeared, a second eyrie hatched two young, both of which died, and the remaining two pairs reared one eaglet each. In 1975, five sites were occupied. One site was found destroyed—the nest pulled to bits and a cairn of stones built on the ledge; a small eaglet mysteriously disappeared from another eyrie; the single egg from a third eyrie was found sucked by crows; the fourth eyrie was deserted early in the season; and the remaining pair reared one eaglet.

The main reason for this sorry record is that the North Uist eagles have no high mountains or much in the way of sizeable cliff on which to nest, and persistently build their eyries in the most absurdly vulnerable and easily accessible places. I have found eyries which could be walked to—one, in fact, was built across a sheep-path on a gradual heather slope, within sight of a road.

The accessibility of the sites makes them liable to disturbance by bird-watchers and photographers, and vulnerable to anyone wishing to steal or smash eggs or take the young. Eagles are traditionally persecuted by local shepherds, who believe that their sheep and lambs are carried off. This will be discussed in a later chapter. Bird-watchers and photographers seldom mean harm, but most eagles are sensitive to disturbance and will desert their eyries if they are visited too often. It is illegal wilfully to disturb eagles at the nest without a licence, and I always think it is a great pity that people should insist on visiting eyries when better and more satisfying views of eagles can often be obtained by watching the adult birds behave naturally from a distance.

Mammals

RED DEER (*Cervus elaphus*)

North Uist supports a herd of about 500 red deer, most of which live in the hill areas of the Lees and Eaval to the south of the island. These areas, being hilly, afford the deer most shelter; also the ground there is less boggy than elsewhere, and the feeding on the better-drained hillslopes is richer than among the acid bogs of the moorland marshes.

For most of the year red deer move in herds, the male deer (stags), segregated from the female deer (hinds). Stags and hinds occupy different ground, but there is a tendency for herds of both sexes to move uphill during summer, away from biting insects and heat; and down into areas of maximum shelter in winter. In early summer, when days may be hot and nights cool, the deer may move considerable distances between feeding and resting areas each day.

Walking across the Uist moors in August, you may come across a herd of hinds basking in a sunny hollow. The deer will be resting; they feed and are generally most active at dawn or dusk. You are unlikely to have seen them before they have noticed you, but if you do happen across an undisturbed hind group, you may notice that it is made up of hinds (antlerless) of all ages, and also some young stags (distinguished by incipient antlers or the scrotal 'bush' under the belly). In fact stags of up to two years of age (when they are called 'prickets') move with the hind herds. You may also notice that while some of the animals are resting, at least one will be acting as sentry, standing alertly and sniffing continuously for scent of danger. Move unwarily, and she will warn the rest of the herd with a short bark, then lead them in an unhurried but cohesive group out of harm's way. Unless they are very frightened, the deer may keep stopping and turning to look back, their sense of curiosity being quite strong. The hind which gave the alarm is likely to be one of the older, more experienced, hinds of the group.

13. Red deer stags

If, on the other hand, you happen to find a group of stags, you will notice that their behaviour is quite unlike that of the hinds. Any stag group in summer is likely to consist of mature stags of all ages, from the 'pricket' to the old master stag with his impressive spread of antlers. The group you are watching is quite unlikely to have any beast acting as sentry. They will be much less wary than the hind herd, and if you disturb them they will move away as individuals. The stag which has seen you may well be up and off at a bound; but it will make no attempt to warn the others or lead them away. The remaining stags may sense danger and become alert, but they may not be able to trace the source of the disturbance. They will run to and fro in evident bewilderment, perhaps even moving towards danger, until they either settle again or make a loose break for safety, dashing at random across the hillside and not necessarily keeping together.

In August, some of the stags will be in 'hard' antler, but others may have their antlers covered in a fur-like substance known as 'velvet'. This velvet is a living tissue which covers the antlers as they grow, then dies when the antlers have finished growing for that year, usually in August. The velvet is then rubbed off and the bone of the antlers is exposed or 'hard'.

In mid-September, the red deer's breeding or 'rutting' season begins. Stags break away singly from the stag herds and make for the hinds. Each stag will attempt to control a harem of hinds, keeping them in an area he can supervise, and attempting to stop other stags claiming his hinds or the hinds breaking away. A master stag, in control of a large harem, is an imposing animal. In preparation for the rut, he has been feeding well and is in prime condition. His coat is a glossy chestnut-red. His neck is swollen, with a thick mane which gives him a powerful, aggressive appearance. And he has developed a special voice for the rutting—a loud, resonant roar, sometimes trailing off to extraordinary groans and grunts, which he uses to demonstrate to other stags that the territory holding these hinds belongs to him. A challenging stag, attempting to take hinds from one already in possession, will roar to advertise his presence, attracting the master stag to come and protect his harem. Usually such disputes are quickly settled—it is often quite obvious which stag is the stronger, and after a few bellows the weaker stag retires. If the stags are more evenly matched, they may fence lightly with the tips of their antlers, or they may interlock antlers and push each other up or down hill. Stags very rarely inflict serious damage on each other, though cases have been recorded where two stags' antlers have become inextricably interlocked and the unfortunate creatures have died of starvation.

A rutting stag feeds hardly at all. He spends his whole time tearing around the hillside, mating with and gathering his hinds, keeping other stags at bay, occasionally wallowing in peaty hollows and thrashing at heather or rushes with his antlers. Black with peat, his abdomen shrinking from lack of food, he will lose condition and after a fortnight he will go off alone, leaving his hind group to be taken over by another stag or broken up amongst a number of stags. By the end of October the stags are back in their peaceful herds, recuperating, and except perhaps for a few very young or small stags which are still attempting to hold hinds, the rutting season is over.

In winter, the red deer of North Uist may come down from the hills towards the machair croftlands, where the feeding is richer. This is especially true in early spring, when the crofters' re-seeding grass and root crops are putting out rich green growth long before the hill grass shows any sign of growing. Until late May groups of red deer, particularly of stags, may invade the agricultural ground, and unless they can be driven off they may cause considerable damage.

In April the stags cast their antlers and immediately begin to grow new ones, protected by the velvet mentioned earlier. They may nibble at the rejected antlers, a source of much needed calcium. From late May onwards until rutting-time, the stags will keep to their own ground, moving higher and further into the moors as the summer proceeds.

The hinds have their calves in late May or early June. The calves are born in sheltered corries or in deep bracken or heather, and when very young are the most endearing creatures imaginable. Dappled for the first few weeks of their lives, they lie curled up at their birthplace, and until they are strong enough to follow their mothers, the hinds return to feed their calves several times each day. If you should find a calf curled up in the heather, please resist the temptation to fondle it. Although the theory that a hind will desert a calf which carries human scent is incorrect, it may happen that a young calf will adopt you as its parent and attempt to follow you, and you'll have great difficulty in getting rid of it!

The deer-stalking season begins on July 1st, and stags may be shot until October 20th. Hinds may be shot between October 21st and February 17th. Adult red deer have no natural predators in Scotland, and in North Uist the only predator at all likely to attack a calf is the golden eagle; there are no foxes in the Outer Hebrides. If the deer were left to their own devices, they would increase in number until they overpopulated the ground and were reduced by disease and starvation. They would also extend their ranges into crofting land and cause increasing amounts of damage to crops. So a judicious culling of red deer is necessary. In most estates in Scotland this is done by commercial shooting—people pay to shoot stags, and are instructed by gamekeepers and ghillies. To maintain a balance of the sexes in the deer stock, and avoid a deterioration in the quality of the animals, hinds are shot by the estate staff when the stag-shooting season is over.

In North Uist, commercial deer-shooting is not really a viable proposition. There are bigger and better and more accessible deer-forests on the Scottish mainland, and freight-charges make it expensive to send venison to the mainland for sale. The numbers of deer have to be controlled, and as far as is possible the herd is kept in balance by the staff of North Uist estates.

SEALS

The seal most frequently seen off the western coasts of North Uist is the grey or Atlantic seal (*Halichoerus grypus*). The common seal (*Phoca vitulina*) occurs as well but not so often off the exposed western shores as in the tidal inlets of the island's east coast. There is always some confusion in identifying the two species, but given a good view, the long-nosed profile of the grey seal contrasts with the round-headed 'snub-nosed' profile of the common seal. The latter is also much smaller and though its colours are variable, its closely mottled appearance is distinctive in comparison with the smooth grey or brown of the Atlantic species, which has patches, not mottles, of darker colour on its underside.

The grey seal is in fact a very rare animal. The majority of the whole world population breeds in British waters, and by far the largest part of these breed on uninhabited oceanic islands off the Scottish coast. Orkney and Shetland hold large numbers, but the largest colony of any one island is that of North Rona, where some 8000 seals gather and 3000 calves are born annually. This represents about one-seventh of the world population of grey seals.

North Rona lies in the Atlantic north-west of the Outer Hebridean island of Lewis. The other major Hebridean breeding ground for grey seals is the scatter of islands in, or to the west of, the Sound of Harris—mainly Shillay, Gasker and Haskier. North Uist possesses two main colonies—Heiskeir, or the Monach Islands, where about 100 calves are born each year, and Causamul, a tiny rocky island about two miles (3.2 km) from the mainland near Hougharry, producing about fifty calves annually.

In contrast common seals haul out in pairs or small groups to calve on skerries or sand-banks. They are generally distributed in the larger east coast inlets of North Uist, notably Locheport, Lochportain and Loch Mhicphaill. The calves are born with a short, tough coat, and they can swim almost from birth—which usually occurs in April or May. The calves then stay with the adults in pleasant family groups for several months.

Grey seals, however, begin to gather round their breeding stations in July. They rest in numbers on surrounding skerries, until the bulls come to land at the end of August and take possession of territories within the breeding area. When they first haul out, the bulls are massively fat, weighing 5 cwt (254 kg) or more, but while they are in the possession of territories, often for as long as a month, they do not feed, and lose weight and condition rapidly.

The cows haul out during September and October, come into the bulls' territories and give birth within a few days. The calves are blind and helpless, and for at least the first three weeks of their lives they are covered in a coat of white, silky hair quite unsuitable for swimming. Grey seal cows are very attentive parents, but in the congestion of the colony, and particularly if the breeding site is threatened by high tides, mortality amongst the calves is very high. The seals of the Monach Islands and Causamul both have colonies on slabby rocks near sea-level, and both may lose many calves to the high tides and rough seas of that time of year.

The grey seal calves moult their silky coats for a more seaworthy covering while weaning, and as soon as they achieve this, they are deserted by the adults, which mate, then disperse slowly. The calf, fed for three weeks or so on the extremely rich milk of its mother, is hugely corpulent, and may lie about on the rocks for up to a month after weaning before it makes its way to the sea. Some adults and calves will stay and feed around their breeding

Fig. 22 Grey seal pup (*Halichoerus grypus*)

stations: others disperse as far afield as Iceland and Scandinavia, or as far south as the coasts of Spain.

Common seal calves, on the other hand, are able to swim at birth, and they stay with their parents until they are comparatively strong and capable, which may explain why they can breed successfully in a variety of situations which could not be used by grey seals. This may be a reason for the wider distribution and greater success of the common seal as a species, and it has been said that their breeding habits represent a step in advance of the evolutionary stage of the more restricted grey seal.

The appearance and habits of both species of seal stir the imagination, and it's hardly surprising that legends involving seals are legion among the islands. The human appearance, especially marked in the common seal, has given rise to stories in which seals represent the souls of dead islanders, or change into human shape. A certain MacCodrum of Hougharry saw a cow-seal in her human form and stole her seal-skin. She became his wife and bore him several children. But when one of the children revealed the whereabouts of the hidden skin, MacCodrum's wife slipped into it and returned to the Atlantic whence she came.

Nowadays the legends are rarely believed and are regarded simply as local folklore. But there is still a magic about the seals, and it is pleasing to hear them moaning from the skerries throughout a fine summer twilight, or see them basking like great blissful cigars on sun-warmed rocks.

OTHER MAMMALS
Apart from deer and seals, North Uist is not notable for its mammalian wildlife. Foxes, weasels, stoats, badgers and hedgehogs are all absent. The only wild mammal predator is the otter (*Lutra lutra*), which is numerous, though rarely seen because of its nocturnal habits. The coasts of North Uist, with sheltered inlets leading into freshwater lochs, is ideal otter habitat. They can situate their breeding 'holts' in sea-cliffs or on offshore islands where they are unlikely to be disturbed, and their food supply is plentiful and varied. They may take sea-fish, or trout and eels from the freshwater lochs, or in times of hard weather they may feed on shell-fish in the tidal pools. Never entirely restricted to a marine diet, otters may kill and eat rodents and birds. On more than one occasion they have caused great destruction among gull or tern colonies, for, like foxes, when roused they

will kill for pleasure and not merely to eat. Otters on the west coast have an abundant and easily available food supply in spring, when the machair and machair marshes are teeming with young birds. Many a brood of ducklings or wader chicks falls prey to them; I have seen them teasing incubating swans on a machair loch, and on one occasion I saw a dog otter carrying a dead rabbit across an area of marsh.

The lack of mammalian ground-predators is one of the reasons for the vast populations of rabbits on North Uist's machair. The sandy turf is ideal for burrowing, and there are huge warrens in the sand-dunes of all machairs. Though myxomatosis recurs every year, rabbit populations recover very quickly and every spring there are huge numbers. Rabbits inhabit the moors up to the extreme hill summits, and it is possible that the rabbits which live at a higher altitude escape myxomatosis and act as a reservoir for machair populations. Before myxomatosis, rabbits were often trapped or shot and regarded by the people of North Uist as a welcome source of meat. Since myxomatosis, fewer rabbits are shot for the table. Rabbits are a food less for humans than for predatory or scavenging birds, and for the feral cats which breed out on the machair and return to eat rats and mice round the townships during the winter.

Rats and rabbits can achieve plague proportions on the island, but other rodent species are not so evident. Brown and blue hares are both present though not numerous; the most commonly seen mouse is a field-mouse of a sub-species confined to the Outer Hebrides, being larger than the mainland mouse and smaller than St. Kilda's more famous sub-species. The short-tailed vole, which feeds short-eared owls and other birds of prey, is another sub-species confined to the Outer Isles.

Invertebrates

The high proportion of water to land makes North Uist notable for aquatic or semi-aquatic animals other than birds. Of the insects that infest the island, the biting midge is the most likely to force its attentions on the visitor. Countless millions of these tiny creatures breed in the bogs and marshes, and from June to the first gales or frosts in September or early October, they can make any outdoor activity impossible. Most active before sunrise and after sunset, the midges prefer calm, damp conditions, and are more of a feature of the inland moors than the drier, windier machair. To anyone who has suffered severely from midges, it can be very little consolation to learn that it is the female of one main species (*Culicoides impunctatus*) which bites, requiring blood to make its eggs fertile.

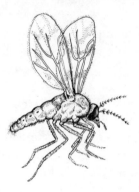

Fig. 23 Midge (*Culicoides impunctatus*)

Another creature which can attack humans is the sheep-tick, a small flat-bodied parasite which burrows into the skin of domestic animals. After hatching from eggs in the heather, a tick larva, so tiny as to be almost invisible, climbs a stalk or stem and waits for a sheep, cow, deer or other animal to pass. It then attaches itself to its host, walks round until it finds a place where the skin is suitably thin, and burrows in. When gorged with blood, the larva drops off into the heather again, undergoes metamorphosis into a second larval stage and again waits for an animal host. After three such larval stages, the tick is adult, and the female is about the size of a match-head. When engorged, she swells considerably, and while feeding she may be fertilised by the smaller, wandering male. Eventually she drops off the host and lays her eggs in the heather. Ticks can parasitise moorland animals in large numbers, hanging in clusters from the undersides or eyelids of sheep and cattle, and severe infestation can cause disease or death to the host. The moors of North Uist shelter unusually large numbers of these ticks, and anyone habitually walking through heather will occasionally find them contentedly embedded in his ankles. They are irritating but harmless to humans, and can usually be nipped out with finger nails or forceps.

The island's short, windy summers are not attractive to butterflies, but common blues (*Lycaena icarus*) and green-veined whites (*Pieris napi*) inhabit the machair, while meadow browns (*Maniola jurtina*), and the large and small heaths (*Coenonympha tullia* and *Coenonympha pamphilus*) can be found on the moors. Moths with heather-eating larvae sometimes occur in great numbers, the most common being the eggar (*Lasiocampa quercus*), drinker (*Cosmotriche potatoria*) and magpie moths (*Abraxas grossulariata*). I have seen hatches of the last species so huge that each step through the heather sent up the moths like thistle-down. Bumble-bees and flies replace butterflies on the machair. The bees are of several species and favour especially the masses of clover and charlock in their season. Flies thrive on the sea-shores, breeding and feeding on the carrion and seaweed of the tide-lines, and infesting the dense stands of umbelliferous machair plants in mid-summer.

Fig. 24 Common blue (*Lycaena icarus*)
Fig. 25 Magpie caterpillar and moth (*Abraxas grossulariata*)

Freshwater fish

Feeding the water-birds and eating the insects of the lochs are the island's freshwater fish. Brown trout (*Salmo trutta*) are present in most of the lochs, but are largest in the richer, less acid machair waters where eels also abound. Sea-trout run via tidal inlets into the lochs, and are the main reason for North Uist's popularity with fishermen. North Uist Estates control most of the fishing, issuing permits from their office in Lochmaddy, and hiring out boats on the larger lochs. The waters are managed for fishing, river-watchers are employed when the trout are running, and there is a small trout hatchery at Langass. Salmon (*Salmo salar*) do run into North Uist waters, but because the rivers are short and are not suitable for spawning, they are neither numerous nor large.

Wildlife and crofting

The wildlife of almost all regions in the world is influenced greatly by man, and that of North Uist is no exception. Here, the most intense human activity is the cultivation of the machair, which involves ploughing the natural grassland and sowing with corn. This affects machair wildlife in a number of ways, but it may be said that such agricultural practice is so traditional that the ecological situation has adapted to it. The flora of the island would no doubt become more varied were ploughing and grazing to cease, but we have to recognise that the grain which feeds the people also feeds many wild animals. Dense flocks of small birds feed on the corn while it stands ripe or in small stacks. Meadow pipits, skylarks, corn-buntings and twites gather on the fields, and with them come the predatory birds to feed on them—short-eared owls, merlins, hen-harriers, buzzards and pere-grines. Greylag geese, which breed in the island interior, bring their young down to the grain in August and crofters complain that they trample on it.

The machair marshes are a different proposition. They are a unique habitat, of extreme botanical and zoological interest, and they may be threatened by drainage schemes which could convert them to rough pasture for grazing. The finest surviving marsh lies between the townships of Hougharry and Balranald, and is the main reason why the Royal Society for the Protection of Birds has a reserve there. But other marshes are diminished or have already gone.

On the moorlands, the greatest effect of man's activity is shown in the lack of trees. The strong salt-laden winds reduce tree-growth, but sheep are the main destroyers of the scrub woodland which, if left to survive, could add

14. Balranald Bird Reserve

variety to the island's wildlife. Experimental plantations were situated on Ben Langass and above the Sollas–Bayhead road eight years ago, and the trees, after a slow start, are surviving and showing signs of growth.

Sheep are also responsible for the crofters' predominantly hostile attitude towards eagles, and this most magnificent of our birds has suffered persecution, while numbers of other scavenging species, such as ravens, crows and gulls, have benefited from carrion in the shape of dead sheep and lambs.

Every rural community to some extent uses its environment. Apart from agriculture, the people of North Uist may reap an occasional harvest of gulls' eggs or shoot wildfowl in their season. Such activities are never carried to excess, and it may be that the unique ecology of North Uist is less endangered by traditional land-use than by increased pressure from outside the island.

Tourism is not a major industry in North Uist. The weather is too uncertain, the facilities are too few. Accommodation is scarce and rarely advertised. But it is a fact that more and more people are coming to the island each summer, and an unusually high proportion of the visitors are interested in natural history. Herein is a conflict. As the number of visitors increases, the wildlife is more and more disturbed. But at the same time, as more people become aware of the island's exceptionally interesting ecology, support for its conservation grows. One can only hope that the interest in conservation is great enough to protect the island's wildlife from any future threat.

3. The People of the Island

Looking over North Uist's landscape we can immediately recognise that the scenery of the Western machair is agricultural, much affected by man. His fences enclose pasture-land and hayfields around the settlements, which are themselves conspicuously scattered along the roadside and not concealed by hedges and trees. The machair itself is obviously used; in summer there are regular patches of grain crops, and in winter grazing animals roam over the still evident marks of the previous year's ploughing.

Inland, man's influence is not so obvious and there are no marks of agriculture: few grazing animals, no habitations. Yet even this seemingly 'natural' landscape owes much of its appearance to man's past and present activity.

History

The first human settlement of North Uist was probably by Mesolithic, or Middle Stone Age, peoples, at about 3800 B.C. They, in fact, did little to change the landscape of the time. At that date, the Hebrides were enjoying a warmer climate than they have at present, and we may guess that the islands were quite densely forested by hazel and birch. The Mesolithic people were not agriculturists; they were nomadic hunters and fishermen, possibly few in number, and living in small family groups in caves, on islands, and in rough shelters on the sea-shore. During the winter they probably lived largely on shellfish from coastal rocks and pools. They grew no crops, and kept no animals, so their effect on the wooded landscape was minimal.

Several hundred years after the coming of the Mesolithic people, the

Neolithic or New Stone Age peoples began to arrive. Their way of life was rather more advanced, and with their improved tools they were able to clear ground for crops. The most obvious remaining evidence of habitation by these peoples is their rudimentary pottery kilns on an island of Loch nan Geirann, and more particularly, a number of their burial-places, or 'chambered cairns'. The best example of a Neolithic chambered cairn is Barpa Langass, south of the Clachan–Lochmaddy road, on the slope of Ben Langass. From the road it looks merely a huge heap of stones, but go up to it by a path from the roadside and you will find that the cairn has a central domed chamber, entered by a low, east-facing passageway. There are other such chambered cairns in North Uist, and I rather like the one under Marragh, at the head of Loch Scadavay. Though less well preserved and smaller than Barpa Langass, it occupies an attractive position on a knoll overlooking the island's centre with its maze of lochs.

The New Bronze Age gave way to the Iron Age, but the first major innovation came about with the arrival of the Celtic peoples who had been moving west through Europe for many hundreds of years. The Celts cleared and ploughed land, and kept sheep, cattle, horses and goats. They left evidence of occupation in their buildings, which were mainly of three types: duns, brochs, and wheelhouses. A 'dun' is essentially a stone-built fortification, consisting usually of a high stone wall enclosing a small area and living quarters for a few families. There are remains of a great many duns in North Uist, and most typically they were built on freshwater islands, with causeways to the shore. 'Brochs' were rather more elaborate; built as forts, they were circular stone towers of considerable height with concentric galleries running round the walls and linked by short flights of stone steps. Most of the Celtic people, however, lived in 'wheelhouses'. These were fortified only by a circular stone wall a few feet high, roofed by timber and thatch. Inside the wheelhouse was a ring of pillars enclosing a central living area.

The next invasion was by Norsemen from bases in Orkney and Shetland, and the Hebrides remained wholly or partly under Norse rule until they became part of Scotland in the thirteenth century. The Norsemen used wood rather than stone for building, and little evidence of their occupation remains. Other than devastation of woodland, our chief inheritance from them is the place-names, some sixty per cent of which are of Norse origin.

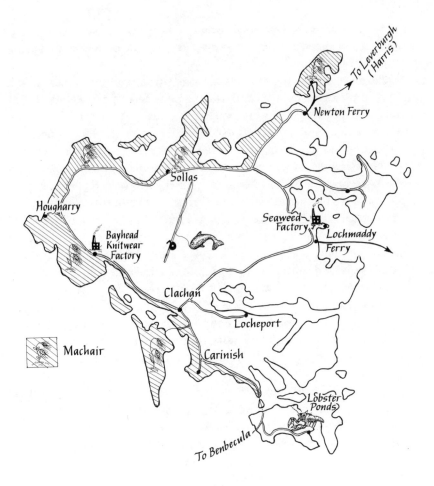

3. Activities, settlements and communications on North Uist

Until the Highland Clearances and the coming of sheep in the mid-nineteenth century, the North Uist economy was based on cattle-farming. The crofting was carried on by the individual members of a clan, holding land for their chief. Oats and barley were grown on the machair in the 'runrig' system, i.e. the arable was divided into strips, each strip worked by a household, and the position of the strips was allocated by drawing lots. They were rectangular in shape, each strip unfenced from the next. During the summer, the animals grazed common hill-ground and pasture. Each household was allowed to have as many cattle grazing on the common land as it could feed in the winter.

While most of the island's income came from cattle-farming, it was common practice for the beef and dairy cattle to be turned on to the hill in summer. To tend the cattle, young men and women of the township went up into the moors with the herds, and lived in rough dwellings known as 'shielings', round which they often grew their own vegetables. Remains of these shielings and this way of life are everywhere across the moors. On dry knolls in the bogs, in sheltered hollows in the hills, always by fresh running water, there are patches of bright green grass on the brown moors, and the tumbled walls of the old shielings. The ground around them was sweetened by manure from animals, and cultivated. Today the sites of shielings are islands of wildflowers in summer. Harebells, heath bedstraw, tormentil and eyebright grow and contrast with the uniform dark vegetation of the moors.

The system of 'crofting' was introduced to the Hebrides, including North Uist, in the eighteenth century. Each household within the township was allocated a 'croft', an area of pasture and arable near the township. In North Uist, the runrig system still operates on the machair, but the individual crofting families also have enclosed crofts on which they may graze animals or grow crops.

It may seem incredible, but in the nineteenth century, North Uist suffered acutely from overpopulation. What land was suitable for cultivation was subdivided among too many people, and poverty and famine were widespread. Reduction in population was necessary, but it was achieved by the authorities of the time through appallingly inhuman means. Some people left willingly, but others were evicted from their homes, and the hardship and bitter feeling which this caused are still remembered. In place of the people, sheep were introduced on a large scale. In 1886, after much militancy, the Crofters' Holding Act was instituted, which gave the crofters security of tenure, and established the Crofters' Commission, a governmental body which supervises crofting methods throughout Scotland. The population of North Uist has continued to decline, slowly, until the present.

15. 'White' houses near Valley Strand

Crofting and the community

The main landowner in North Uist is Lord Granville of North Uist Estates. Lord Granville lives in the north of the island, at Griminish, but the estate is largely run from the office in Lochmaddy, where a factor is in control of day to day affairs. North Uist Estates own most of the central moorland and hill area, but much of the machair and crofting land is owned by the Department of Agriculture for Scotland, which has an office in Benbecula. Apart from a few areas of freehold, most of the crofters rent their land from one or other of these landlords. Most crofting families nowadays live in modern or modernised houses equipped with every convenience. A minority of thatched cottages are still occupied, however, and the various types of dwelling can sometimes be seen in and around the townships. 'Black' houses were stone-walled without mortar, they rarely had windows, and the thatch did not overlap the top of the outer walls, so that rain ran into the wall itself. These were superseded by 'white' houses, which had windows, and a thatch overlapping the outer walls. Later, mortar was introduced, houses became less like low domes and more angular, and slate roofing replaced thatch. When a family had removed to an improved house, the tendency was to use the old structure as a byre for animals until it fell derelict. In some places successive styles in housing are found on the same plot of land—a couple of ruined, roofless byres standing near the new-style house in which the family now live. Two 'white' houses remain occupied and in excellent shape on the mainland shore of Vallay Strand.

The township is the most significant feature of North Uist's social and agricultural life. We have already seen that most crofting settlement occurs on the machair, but driving along the main road of the island through the crofting areas, it is often difficult to say where one township ends and another begins. There are no compact villages or hamlets; the houses are strung out along the roadsides all the way, so that the nature of the township is not immediately clear.

It is in fact a community of crofters. There may be up to, say, twenty families involved, and each family will have a house; a croft (i.e. a piece of private land around or near the house); and a share of the township's common land. In a typical machair township, the house will have easy access to a road and will have its 'croft' around it; this is why the houses are rarely together, but are strung out along roadsides, each separated from the next by the crofts. The township of Hougharry, in north-west North Uist, is an exception to this rule. At the time of the Highland Clearances, the local township was situated further west, on the headland of Ard an Runair, now part of the Royal Society for the Protection of Birds' reserve at Balranald. It was considered necessary to remove the village and turn the rocky headland into a sheep-walk, and the inhabitants were given the choice of having their new houses built either each on its croft or together, separate from the crofts. The people of Ard an Runair chose to have their houses together, and this is why Hougharry, alone among North Uist's machair townships, has a conventional 'village' appearance, the houses grouped picturesquely on a headland between two bays. The township crofts are inland of the houses, each family's croft enclosed by a fence.

The common land, shared among the members of the township, will consist of an area of machair and an area of hill ground. Typically, the houses are placed where 'machair' borders on 'hill', so the machair is west of the houses, or towards the sea, and the hill is to east, or towards the central moors.

The machair grassland is ploughed in March and early April. The ploughing is done in sections, and within each section one family will be responsible for one long, narrow strip. The position of the family's strip changes from section to section, so that no single family will monopolise good ground, or suffer from having poorer ground than other families of the township. Most families own a tractor and a plough, the plough being specially adapted for use under machair conditions. Two tines make a double furrow at each sweep, and the blades of the plough can be raised or lowered as they pass over stony or uneven ground.

After ploughing comes sowing, which is done by hand. The sower walks slowly along the furrows with a bag of grain over his shoulder, and as he walks he rhythmically scatters grain to right and left. Ideal conditions for sowing are calm days, so that the grain doesn't blow around or the sandy soil move, destroying the furrows and burying the grain. The grain sown is traditionally a mixture of oats and rye; the oats are the valuable crop, but left alone in the weather conditions of the island, they would be stunted, and give poor yield. Rye is more tolerant of salty winds and sandy soil, and as it grows it tends to draw the oats up with it towards the light, and protects them from wind.

The next task on the machair is the fertilisation of the crop. Seaweed was the traditional fertiliser, having a dual purpose in that it gave body to the sandy soil as it rotted down, and provided nitrates to sweeten the ground. Most crofters now use chemical fertilisers, because this saves having to cart bulky loads of seaweed from the shore, and they are helped in buying the fertiliser by a government subsidy. There is a body of opinion, however, which says that the use of chemical fertiliser eventually causes deterioration of the machair, as it boosts growth unnaturally, depriving the soil of both minerals and substance, and increasing the likelihood of wind-blow across the ploughed areas.

Spring is often cold and windy in the Hebrides, and the corn doesn't appear much until May, when it is fertilised. July and August are warmer and wetter, and long hours of daylight help the corn to grow quickly. The

16. Harvest scene, Balranald machair

great danger is from wind in August or September, which may flatten the corn before it is harvested.

Harvest occurs in late September, and is dominated by the weather. It is an uncertain time of the year, and equinoctial gales with rain may cause delay. I have seen crofters saving what they can of their wind-flattened crops, cutting with scythes during moonlit nights in November. Most families own a binding machine, which cuts the corn and binds it into small sheaves. Aware of the constant threat of bad weather, whole families take part in the cutting and stacking. One person drives the tractor drawing the binder, another operates levers on the binder to raise and lower the cutting blades over uneven ground. Wives and children may be propping the small sheaves into groups of four or six for the wind to dry before they are gathered into larger stacks. Eventually, the larger stacks are moved and brought together into even larger stacks; these are placed near the houses, and used to feed the cattle during the winter.

Hebridean cornfields usually contain a large proportion of weeds; corn marigolds and charlock are the most prevalent, and although they beautify the fields with swathes of brilliant yellow, they can impair the quality of the harvest, the thick green stems refusing to dry quickly and often jamming the binding machines.

The machair land is ploughed in a three-year rotation; i.e. the strips are ploughed and sown for three years, and at the end of the third year are sown with grass and clover. During the fourth year, the strips lie fallow. Rotation is usually operated on a strip-by-strip basis, but Balranald township, with their large and comparatively uniform machair, simplify things by splitting their machair into two, ploughing all of one half for three years, then moving to the other half for the next three years.

17. While the sun shines: haymaking on the machair

18. Machair agriculture: strips of corn, sand-dunes beyond

Agriculture on the machair obviously depends very much on the close community system based on the township. All members of the township practise fundamentally the same methods, and they all operate at the same time. Given a fine day in April, the deserted, wintry machair suddenly blossoms with people as everyone takes advantage of the weather to get the ploughing done. Everywhere on the machair there are tractors pulling ploughs and sowers walking up and down the furrows, and over them all fly great flocks of gulls following the ploughs. The members of the township co-operate for the good of all; some people, for instance, may not own ploughs or binders, but they can expect to be helped out by the more fortunate so that no one in the community suffers.

The corn is used wholly as fodder for the island's domestic stock; none is exported. During the winter, cattle and sheep graze the machair, feeding amongst the stubble of the past harvest. The members of the township take it in turn to tend them, and in May they are moved out to the hill away from

19. Cattle feeding on a beach

the growing corn. Each crofter keeps his cattle on the common land, but most people also have a few head of stock on their own crofts.

Since crofting activity demands considerable co-operation and agreement between the members of the community, a system of township government has been evolved. A township clerk is elected and holds office for three years; his duty is to act as administrator and present matters which demand township agreement to the vote of the members.

The agricultural economy of North Uist is based on the rearing of beef cattle. This is the traditional activity, and prices at the cattle sales, held in autumn and spring, control the crofter's annual income. Hebridean cattle are not 'Highland', but are a blend of Highland and island strains which gives a breed called 'Luing'; some of the breed show the shaggy, wide-horned Highland strain more strongly than others. The calves are particularly valued, and mainland buyers come to the sales to buy these animals, which are in peak condition after having spent a summer on rich island grazing, before they have lost condition by having endured an island winter.

Sheep-farming has been widespread only since the Clearances, but now a crofter receives a government subsidy for every sheep he owns. This subsidy makes sheep-farming more directly profitable than cattle-farming, and so the sheep are often kept on the best pasture, to the exclusion of cattle, and there is always a temptation for a crofter to keep more sheep than is good for the land. Sheep crop grass with their teeth, and nibble very close to the ground, whereas cattle tear the grass with their long tongues. So the sheep reduce vegetation to a minimum, and because their droppings are acid, they can make the land on which they graze sour and unproductive. Some crofters are beginning to take note of how the quality of their machair is deteriorating and becoming more susceptible to sand-blow because of overgrazing by sheep, and future years may see a return to cattle-farming.

Apart from oats and rye, the main crop grown on the machair is potatoes. Planting is usually carried out in spring, and the ground is prepared by first spreading seaweed, which is ploughed in as the potatoes are planted. The crop is again entirely for home consumption, and in the autumn the potatoes are picked and laid in pits for use during the winter. Potatoes grow very well in the light, sandy soil; in fact root crops in general tend to thrive, and it is possible that vegetable gardening could succeed, if there were a demand for the produce. The growing of vegetable and salad food is not traditional; emphasis has always been on grazing for stock, and although the introduction of refrigerators and deep-freezes would now make it possible for the islanders to grow and keep vegetables for home use, very few of them do so. Vegetable gardening is left to incoming people who have a taste for such food, and as the tourist trade is still small, guest-houses and shops don't demand vegetables in sufficient quantity to make growing for sale a profitable proposition.

The people and the sea

Compared with other Scottish Highland and island areas, the land of North Uist is relatively rich, and this may be the reason for an emphasis on crofting rather than sea-fishing. Attempts have been made to boost the fishing industry, but the fact remains that on the western coast, where people live,

20. Sheep-shearing. Most of the island sheep are clipped by hand

suitable ports are few. The problem of export is a major one; the fish has to be sent to market on the mainland, and in large quantities, to compete with more advanced fishing industries elsewhere. There is no tradition of commercial fishing among the islanders, though in the crofting townships of the west coast, each township may have one or two lobster boats, owned by individuals and often crewed by single families. People in areas where the land is poorer turn more readily to the sea, and there is a higher proportion of boats per head of population at Lochportain, in the north-east, and at Grimsay, an island connected to south-east North Uist by a causeway. Lochportain and Grimsay have very poor crofting land with little or no machair, and Grimsay is especially sea-inclined because it stands round a sheltered natural port.

Virtually no one fishes for fish. Not because the fish aren't there—the coasts of North Uist are as rich in herring, mackerel, haddock and flatfish as anywhere in the north. But the market doesn't exist.

Home consumption alone could not keep the boats afloat, and no one seems inclined to set up a fishing or fish-processing industry when the markets are so far away and the land-loving islanders themselves so uninterested. The fishing industry is based on lobsters, which are taken in pots around the island and sold to the ponds at Grimsay, where they are kept in tanks for export. There is possibly no finer lobster fishing-ground in Europe than the Hebridean seaboard, and in good conditions a boat can earn its crew a great deal of money in a short time. There are two problems. First, the inshore waters are becoming over-fished and the lobsters are getting scarce. Second, weather conditions are such that fishing is quite impossible between mid-September and mid-April, and during the remaining five months a fisherman may consider himself lucky if he can get to sea for an average of more than two or three days a week. Because of the scarcity of lobsters in inshore waters, the fishermen are forced further out, where seas are rougher and more dangerous, and they may have to compete with boats from mainland or foreign ports. The only answer is for fishing to be done by bigger and stronger boats, and this in fact is happening. Helped by government subsidies, a fisherman may buy a larger boat with a more powerful engine, a cabin, and modern radar devices for depth-sounding and navigation. Looking to the future, it is possible that the small open boat laying pots round the island rocks, depending greatly on inherited and intimate knowledge of local conditions, will eventually be superseded by fewer and larger boats, co-operatively owned and capable of fishing the open Atlantic.

The small open boats return to harbour every day. The fishermen of Grimsay are exceptional in that some boats base themselves on Heiskeir, a group of islands 8 miles (12.9 km) west of North Uist. Heiskeir is now a National Nature Reserve, but during the season the fishermen live out there for five days of the week, sharing the island's single remaining house with the Nature Conservancy.

The sea-pools of the rocky shores abound with edible winkles, which may be collected and sold, like lobsters, to the ponds at Grimsay. Winkles gather between high and low water-marks, most abundantly under the seaweed in pools, but also over shingle and on the rocks. Picking is usually done for two hours before and for two hours after low tide, and is an arduous business. Winter is the most popular season, as the people are otherwise occupied during the rest of the year, and it's a wet, chilly process to grope around bare-handed in pools at this time. It can be heavy work, too: a winkler may gather for several days before taking his pickings for sale, and he may keep his winkles fresh by leaving them in hessian sacks in the pools. Lifting and carrying the dripping sacks across slippery rocks to suitable keeping pools or to a vehicle some distance away make winkling no sinecure. Even then the work isn't finished. The winkles have to be washed and sorted to remove sand, stones, whelks and hermit crabs. Whelks and hermit crabs may be picked by mistake, but are inedible and are rejected at weighing-in at the ponds. Hermit crabs are a great nuisance, as they may inhabit winkle shells and be difficult to spot. Packed in a sack of winkles, the hermit crabs are quick to realise that all isn't well, and they leave their adopted shells. Once out of the shells they die, and within hours they can create an offensive smell out of all proportion to their size. A couple of overlooked hermit crabs in a sack of winkles can result in the whole sack being condemned as rotten at the weighing-in station. The current price for winkles fluctuates between £3 and £4 a hundredweight (50.8 kg), but the heavy work and the discomfort, plus the fact that accessible areas are limited and can be picked only once in a season, make the work unpopular, and it isn't carried on now so much as formerly.

Rock fishing as practised by the islanders is a pleasanter occupation. In good weather it can be quite idyllic. Dense shoals of laithe, saithe and coalfish come into the coastal bays in autumn, and the first sign that the fish are present is usually the gathering of predatory animals to feed on them. Gannets will be plunging into the shoals at the water's edge; gulls will sit and simply scoop until they are replete; cormorants, shags and auks collect for the feast and there may well be a couple of common or grey seals in attendance. These predators enjoy easy feeding for a while and, given the opportunity to gorge, they do so. Cormorants and shags stand dyspeptically on rocks with crops distended, gulls sit on the water too gorged to fly.

The shoals move close inshore at high tide, and a coastal township may have its favoured rock from which the people fish, using long bamboo canes, a fixed line with a cork float and, for bait, rotten winkles on a number of hooks. The method is apparently to throw your line out, then watch the float

21. Seaweed deposited on a beach

intently. As soon as the float bobs you snatch up the line, and if you're lucky you may have a fish on every hook. Laithe and saithe can grow quite large—up to two feet (0.6 m) long—but the most common catch is coalfish, which are baby saithe, small, silvery, and locally called 'cuddies'. Hauls of cuddies can be quite prodigious, and after a good night's fishing they may be distributed freely around the community. Rolled whole in oatmeal, and fried crisp within an hour of catching, they're delicious. From the east coast of the island, this recreational type of fishing may be done from small boats, using baited lines and rubber eels. Catches in the eastern inlets may include numbers of mackerel and haddock.

Another important and traditional industry carried on along the coasts is the collection and processing of seaweed. At one time, kelp-burning was vital to the island's economy. In fact during the second half of the eighteenth century kelp-burning was probably the main source of income. The main types harvested were deep-sea tangles and wrack-weeds, and these were burned to give an alkaline ash used in the manufacture of soap. When alternative methods of producing the required ash were found to be cheaper, the kelp industry declined and by the mid-nineteenth century was almost non-existent. Interest revived in the middle of the present century, however, and Alginate industries opened a seaweed-processing factory in Lochmaddy in 1957. The weed may be collected from the coastal rocks at low tide, or it can be picked off western beaches where it has been piled by high winter seas and gales. A few people work in the seaweed-processing factory, and a few more are permanently employed as collectors. Islanders on the west coasts gather the weed into heaps along the beaches, where it can be sold wet or dried to the factory. On the east coast, people go out in boats, cut the weed and use nets to tow it ashore in huge rafts. At the factory the weed is dried, ground, and exported for use as a thickening agent in the manufacture of food and cosmetics.

Peat as fuel

Despite the introduction of electricity in 1969, and the fact that coal is brought over by ferry, the traditional cutting of peat for fuel is very much a part of island life. Before the time of motor vehicles and tarmac roads, the township peat-banks were often situated far in the hills behind the townships, and the peats were carried by horse and cart. Now that the horse as a means of transport has been replaced by motor cars and tractors, which cannot negotiate the soft moorland tracks to the old peat-beds, most of the peat-banks lie within easy access of a road. They occur wherever suitable cutting areas adjoin the main road round the island, but the principal area is to each side of the road from Lochmaddy to Clachan, which runs for eight miles across a comparatively level peat-bog. Another road which crosses the island's interior runs from Bayhead on the western machair to Sollas in the north, and there are considerable peat-cuttings at the flat western end of the road, before it winds up into the hills.

The peat-banks run at right angles to the roads so that as many as possible can be easily reached. Cutting is usually done in spring, the dryest time of the year, and given reasonable conditions in April or May, the crofters will go out and make a start. Each cutting is about 18 inches (0.45 m) wide and between 100 and 150 yards (90–137 m) in length, and to a depth of two peats. The first task is to strip off the surface layer of heather, grass and sphagnum, to expose the suitable peat. This is called 'turfing', and the turfs are thrown into the bank neatly, so that they will eventually form a cuttable surface for future peat-banks. For although the amount of peat on the island is almost infinite, suitable areas adjacent to roads are not, and conservation measures are necessary if peat-cutting is to be convenient enough to continue. The peat is exposed as a shiny, black shelf which is cut into brick-shaped pieces and thrown out on to the heather to dry. Good peat cuts like firm, moist cheese into convenient slices. A special spade, or knife, is used; straight-handed with a vertical wedge-shaped blade, it is pushed into the peat-shelf by one person, and with one action a brick of peat is levered out for the other member of the working pair to catch and throw out. The work is rhythmical, and when performed by people familiar with the technique, it can be done very quickly. It is said that two people can cut enough peat for a year in two days, but cutting it is only part of the process. The peats are thrown out flat and, given two or three days' drying weather, the crofter will return and make them into small stacks to dry out completely. Eventually they are brought to the roadside, where they are usually restacked for collection. When finally brought to the house, the peat is stacked carefully into the domed heaps which are so much a feature of island townships. The stacks are so arranged that rain cannot penetrate them, and dry peats are always available though the stacks are outdoors. Peat varies in quality. The best is non-fibrous and the colour of plain chocolate; it burns slowly with very little flame, emitting much heat and leaving a fine, dust-like ash. At the other end of the scale of quality is the fibrous peat which is difficult to cut, shrinks when dried, and burns quickly away.

Peat-cutting is hard work and is best done at a time when crofting families are already fully occupied with ploughing, sowing, and lambing. There is a growing tendency for crofters to burn a mixture of coal and peat, or even to burn coal only. But the fact remains that at a time when fuel is scarce, peat is freely available and very cheap, and it is likely that the distinctive smell of peatsmoke will linger around North Uist townships for many years to come.

Present and future

Most people in North Uist live in townships and are engaged in an

22. A peat-bank in central North Uist. South Lee in the background

agricultural way of life which has not fundamentally changed for centuries. It must not be thought, however, that the island society is necessarily 'backward' or 'primitive' by British/European standards, or that it has not changed at all.

Though agricultural methods have altered only slightly, the tradition of one family owning one croft and living off it is disappearing very quickly. It is now accepted that a single croft in itself will not provide its owners with a livelihood. There is a tendency for the small crofts to die out, and the land to be taken into holdings which may include several crofts and machair shares—in fact one household may have shares on the machair of two or more townships.

Another recent tendency is to increasing diversity in activities. Where not so long ago an entire family would be engaged on a single croft, now crofters tend to have profitable sidelines. It was always fairly usual for a crofting family to hold a croft and run a lobster-boat, but now other forms of temporary or part-time employment are available. Women, once tied to the house, may find employment in the Hebridean Knitwear factory, which employs a staff of twenty at Bayhead. Social services employ an increasing number of people, and perhaps the greatest source of non-agricultural employment in recent years has been the army base in Benbecula, where labourers, engineers and domestic staff have been recruited from the local population. There are at present plans for an R.A.F. installation in North Uist which will employ people in non-technical positions.

In the last half-century or so, North Uist has undergone many changes which have made it less isolated. Causeways carry roads over the fords

23. Macbrayne's car ferry *Hebrides* entering Lochmaddy harbour

between North Uist and Benbecula, and Benbecula and South Uist, so that as far as communication is concerned one now tends to think of the Uists and Benbecula as a whole, rather than as separate islands. The road around North Uist, though single-track, is adequately surfaced, as are many of the side-roads leading to formerly remote townships. Macbrayne's ferries run regularly between Lochmaddy, Tarbert in Harris, and Uig in Skye, and the airport at Benbecula brings the island within a few hours' travel of Glasgow or Inverness. Mail travels by air, and a letter posted at a North Uist sub post-office can arrive at its mainland destination next morning.

Perhaps the most influential change in the islanders' way of life arrived with electricity and consequently television. Most islanders are now as much in touch with world events as people anywhere in Britain.

All this modernity has brought some advantages to North Uist. The decline in population which started at the beginning of the nineteenth century is showing signs of coming to an end as islanders have more opportunities of employment locally. There has always been a tendency for young people to leave, some attracted by the glamour of greater sophistication elsewhere, but more simply forced away by lack of employment and opportunity. Young people with academic ability have always had to leave the island for their further education, but although this is still largely true, a modern-style secondary school is now available at Bayhead. Young people now have more choice as to whether to leave or stay, and there are increased opportunities for them to return in later life if they so wish.

The religious denominations in North Uist are mainly the Church of Scotland, the Free Presbyterian Church, and the Free Church of Scotland. Common to these sects is an austerity in worship, a belief in the virtues of toil and a strict moral conventionality. The religion is kept traditional by the fact that the church elders, usually the older and more respected men of the community, elect the ministers and generally have a great deal of authority in the church, and changes are consequently regarded with suspicion. The effect of Sabbatarianism (i.e. the belief in Sunday as a day reserved exclusively for rest and reverence) is often exaggerated by people who write or talk about the Hebrides. While the local population do keep Sunday as a day of rest, there is no Sabbath 'gloom' over North Uist, and no attempt is made to impose Sunday observance on visitors and tourists.

Even more than religion, language controls the way people think, and the individuality of island life is largely due to the fact that Gaelic is still the most commonly spoken language. Religious services are held in Gaelic, and in North Uist, as in the Hebrides generally, there was, until the introduction of the mass media, a strong and distinctive tradition of folk lore and mythology. Today, although Gaelic is taught in schools, there is some sign of decay in the language. In some areas English is spoken almost as much, and where Gaelic *is* used, it survives only in speech. After leaving school, the islanders rarely write in the traditional language.

North Uist is a small island with a small population, very near to one of the most densely populated and 'advanced' countries of the world. In some ways close communication with mainland Britain is to its advantage; its insular position and unproductive soils discourage development, so that without governmental subsidies the islanders could not live and crofting as a way of life would disappear. On the one hand, North Uist depends on money from the mainland; on the other, traditions and culture are threatened by mainland ideas and standards. It remains to be seen whether the island's people can achieve material prosperity without entirely sacrificing their attractive and distinctive way of life.

Index